THE WORLD
OF
5G
Volume 1
INTERNET OF EVERYTHING

THE WORLD OF 5G
(In 5 Volumes)

THE WORLD OF

Volume 1

INTERNET OF EVERYTHING

Quan Xue
Wenquan Che
South China University of Technology, China

Translator
Lisa Ren
Zhejiang University, China

Proofreader
Lianghe Dong
Mudanjiang Normal University, China

NEW JERSEY • LONDON • SINGAPORE • BEIJING • SHANGHAI • HONG KONG • TAIPEI • CHENNAI • TOKYO

Published by

World Scientific Publishing Co. Pte. Ltd.
5 Toh Tuck Link, Singapore 596224
USA office: 27 Warren Street, Suite 401-402, Hackensack, NJ 07601
UK office: 57 Shelton Street, Covent Garden, London WC2H 9HE

Library of Congress Cataloging-in-Publication Data
Names: Xue, Quan (Telecommunications professor), editor-in-chief.
Title: The world of 5G / authors, Quan Xue, South China University of Technology, China, Wenquan Che, South China University of Technology, China, Jishun Guo, Joyson Intelligent Automotive Research Institute, China, Wei Wu, Skyworth Group Co., Ltd., China, Zhiqiang Xu, Guangzhou Hantele Communication Co., Ltd., China, Wenhua Huang, Southern Medical University, China, Haibin Lin, Affiliated Hospital of Putian University, China.
Description: Singapore ; Hackensack, NJ : World Scientific Publishing Co. Pte. Ltd, [2022] | Includes bibliographical references and index. | Contents: v. 1. Internet of everything -- v. 2. Intelligent manufacturing -- v. 3. Intelligent home -- v. 4. Intelligent transportation -- v. 5. Intelligent medicine.
Identifiers: LCCN 2021061659 | ISBN 9789811250170 (set ; hardcover) | ISBN 9789811250187 (set ; ebook for institutions) | ISBN 9789811250194 (set ; ebook for individuals) | ISBN 9789811244131 (v. 1 ; hardcover) | ISBN 9789811244148 (v. 1 ; ebook for institutions) | ISBN 9789811244155 (v. 1 ; ebook for individuals) | ISBN 9789811244223 (v. 2 ; hardcover) | ISBN 9789811244230 (v. 2 ; ebook for institutions) | ISBN 9789811244247 (v. 2 ; ebook for individuals) | ISBN 9789811244254 (v. 3 ; hardcover) | ISBN 9789811244261 (v. 3 ; ebook for institutions) | ISBN 9789811244278 (v. 3 ; ebook for individuals) | ISBN 9789811244162 (v. 4 ; hardcover) | ISBN 9789811244179 (v. 4 ; ebook for institutions | ISBN 9789811244186 (v. 4 ; ebook for individuals) | ISBN 9789811244193 (v. 5 ; hardcover) | ISBN 9789811244209 (v. 5 ; ebook for institutions) | ISBN 9789811244216 (v. 5 ; ebook for individuals)
Subjects: LCSH: 5G mobile communication systems. | Expert systems (Computer science) | Automation.
Classification: LCC TK5103.25 .X84 2022 | DDC 621.3845/6--dc23/eng/20220224
LC record available at https://lccn.loc.gov/2021061659

British Library Cataloguing-in-Publication Data
A catalogue record for this book is available from the British Library.

For any available supplementary material, please visit
https://www.worldscientific.com/worldscibooks/10.1142/12479#t=suppl

Printed in Singapore

Foreword
5G Empowers the Society for Development at a Rapid Speed

Being one of the buzzwords of the global media in recent years, 5G is very attractive because it carries great expectations from people, both in terms of the communication technology itself and the industry changes it could unleash. Recalling the development of human society, technological change is undoubtedly one of the biggest engines. Marked by the invention of the steam engine and electricity, the first two Industrial Revolutions featured mechanization and electrification, respectively. As the wheel of history rolls into the 21st century, a new round of Industrial Revolution featuring intelligence will be looming, and its impact on human civilization and economic development will be no less than that of the previous two Industrial Revolutions. But then what is pushing it? Compared with the previous two, the new Industrial Revolution is no longer pushed by a single technology but instead by the integration of multiple technologies, among which mobile communication, Internet, artificial intelligence, and biotechnology are the decisive elements.

5G, as the commanding heights of modern mobile technology, is an important engine that enables other key technologies mentioned above. Meanwhile, it can also be seen that 5G comes out when the new momentum is needed most by the Internet development. After almost linear rapid growth, the increment rate of China's Internet users is falling with the popularity rate of mobile phones almost refusing to grow. Owning to the fast pace of life, the netizens now pursue new forms of business with short periods, low investments, and quick returns. Faster speed and lower fees have mitigated the cost pressure on broadband Internet access when short videos and small programs are becoming popular. But these are still not enough to meet the requirements of the new format of the Internet. The future development of the Internet calls for new drivers and new models to solve this problem. The industrial Internet, regarded as the second half of the Internet, has just started, and its new driving forces cannot fill deficiencies of the consumer Internet driving force. At present, the Internet enters into a transition period of continuity for new drivers to replace the old ones. At a time when the consumption of the Internet needs to be intensified and the industrial Internet is starting to take off, 5G comes into being.

As the latest generation of cellular mobile communication technology, 5G is characterized by high speed, low latency, wide connectivity, and high reliability. Compared with 4G, 5G's peak rate increases by 30 times, user experience rate advances by 10 times, and spectrum efficiency accelerates by three times. Moreover, compared to 4G, 5G mobile supports high-speed rail with the speed of 500 km/h, with its wireless interface delay reduced by 90%, the connection density enhanced by 10 times, energy efficiency and traffic density improved by 100 times, enough to support the mobile Internet industry and many applications of the Internet. Compared with the previous four generations of mobile communication technologies, the most important change in 5G is the shift from individual-oriented use to industry-oriented applications, providing indispensable high-speed, massive, and low-latency connectivity for Internet of Everything needed by the new round of Industrial Revolution. Therefore, 5G is not only merely a communication technology but also an important "infrastructure".

It is well timed and also quite accountable in cultural inheritance for Guangdong Science and Technology Publishing House to take the lead in organizing the compilation and distribution of this book series and to popularize 5G knowledge in the society for improving the national scientific literacy when the whole society is talking about 5G with great expectations. Compared with the numerous books about 5G in the market, this series stands out with its own characteristics. First of all, Professor Xue Quan, the Chief Editor, who has been focusing on the research of 5G cutting-edge core technologies in recent years, is an expert in the fields of millimeter wave and terahertz. He took the lead in the compilation of this series with his team responsible for the volume, *5G Internet of Everything*, thus aiming to well leverage the tool for the popularization of science to present 5G technology mass-orientally. In addition, with the focus on the integration and application of 5G in the vertical industry, the series comes out just in line with the close social concerns about 5G. The team included industry experts from the Guangdong Provincial Key Laboratory of Millimeter Wave and Terahertz in the South China University of Technology, Automotive Engineering Research Institute of Guangzhou Automobile Group Co., Ltd., Southern Medical University, Guangzhou Hanxin Communication Technology Co., Ltd., Skyworth Group Co., Ltd., for the corresponding volume, respectively. This book series is targeted at the current pain points of the industry, yet contributes to an unfettered imagination of the future of the 5G-enabling industry. It will be an invaluable science book for the public yearning for new technology for a new round of industrial transformation. The first issue of the book series consists of five volumes.

What's remarkable is that while the book focuses on how 5G will revolutionize the vertical industry if integrated with other technologies, it also explores the possible negative effects of technological advances on human beings. In the progress of science and technology, it is essential to stick to human nature, ethics, morality, and law. So the acceleration of the development of science and technology, with "safety valve" and "brake" being indispensable, shouldn't be based on the sacrifice of the dominance of human nature and the thinking ability of human beings. We need to think of science and technology as a "double-edged sword" and better exploit the advantages and avoid disadvantages while turning the passive reaction into an active response.

Coming in with a roar, 5G will have an immeasurable impact on the development of human society. Let's work together and march toward the future.

Wu Hequan
Member of Chinese Academy of Engineering

Foreword
5G as the Engine for Upgrading and Development of the Vertical Industries

As we all know, we are gradually entering a digital era, and many industries and technologies will progress around the data chain, in which the main effect of mobile communication technology is data transmission. Applications that require performance such as high-definition video, multi-device access, and real-time two-way interaction between multiple people are difficult to achieve without the support of high-speed communication technology. As the latest generation of cellular mobile communication technology, 5G features high speed, low delay, wide connection, and high reliability.

The year 2020 marks the first year for 5G commercial use and then the employment of 5G is expected to peak around 2035. 5G will be mainly applied in the following seven fields: smart creation, smart city, smart grid, smart office, smart security, telemedicine and health care, and commercial retail. In these seven fields, it is estimated that nearly 50% of 5G components will be applied to smart creation, while nearly 18.7% will be applied to smart city construction.

The importance of 5G is not only reflected in its great promotion of upgrading industries such as smart creation but also reflected in its direct correlation with the development of artificial intelligence. The development of artificial intelligence requires a large number of user cases and data, and the amount of data that 4G Internet of Things (IoT) can provide for learning is incomparable to that of 5G. Therefore, the development of

5G IoT plays a very important role in promoting the development of artificial intelligence. Relying on 5G can help promote the upgrading of many vertical industries. It is also for this reason that 5G's leading development has become an important engine to promote the development of national science and technology and economy and has also become the focus of competition between China and the United States in the field of science and technology.

Against this background, Guangdong Science and Technology Publishing House took the lead in organizing the compilation and distribution of the "5G World" book series, with the focus on the integrated application and empowerment of 5G in many industries, including manufacturing, medical care, transportation, home furniture, finance, education, and so on. On the one hand, it is a courageous and culturally responsible measure to popularize 5G among the public, enhancing national scientific literacy. On the other hand, this book is also an utterly precious reference for industry insiders who want to understand the trend for the development of 5G technology and industrial integration.

This book series was done under the guidance of Chief Editor, Professor Xue Quan, the Director of the Guangdong Key Laboratory of Millimeter Wave and Terahertz, South China University of Technology. As an expert in the fields of millimeter wave and terahertz technology, Professor Xue Quan will manage to make a book series of popular science with accurate and natural technical features. This book series is scheduled to be publish the first editions of five volumes, including *The World of 5G: Internet of Everything, The World of 5G: Intelligent Manufacturing, The World of 5G: Intelligent Home, The World of 5G: Intelligent Transportation,* and *The World of 5G: Intelligent Medicine.* The compilation team of this series boasts of strong support. In addition to *The World of 5G: Internet of Everything*, which was written by the technical team of Guangdong Millimeter Wave and Terahertz Key Laboratory of South China University of Technology, the other four volumes were mainly written by relevant industry experts. Among all the volumes, *The World of 5G: Intelligent Manufacturing* was written by experts from the Auto Engineering Research Institute of Guangzhou Automobile Group Co., Ltd., while *The World of 5G: Intelligent Medicine* was written by experts from Southern Medical University. *The World of 5G: Intelligent Transportation* was written by Guangzhou Hantele Communication Co., Ltd., and *The World of 5G: Intelligent Home* was written by Skyworth Group Co., Ltd. This kind of cross-industry combination writing team possesses a strong complementary and professional system for the following reasons: for one thing, technical experts can fully grasp the evolution of mobile communication technology and key technologies of 5G; for another, industry experts can accurately feel the pain points of the industry as well as analyze the advantages and challenges of the industries integrated with 5G through incise writing around the central themes to provide a valuable reference for industry peers with real and vivid cases.

Besides a vivid description of the huge changes that could be brought about by the 5G technology merged into industries, what makes this book novel and fresh is the fact that they also discuss the negative effects the rapid advance of technology may have on human beings. The rapid development of high technology should not be done at the cost of human nature, ethics, and thoughts. It is necessary to make sure that technology conforms to science and ethics with the essential "cushion" and "safety valve".

Mao Junfa
Member of Chinese Academy of Sciences

Preface

As a revolutionary leap in technology, 5G provides Internet of Everything with important technical support. Furthermore, it will bring prosperity for mobile Internet and industrial Internet and provide many industries with unprecedented opportunities, thus being expected to trigger profound changes in the whole society. What is 5G? How will 5G empower various industries and promote a new round of Industrial Revolution? The answers can be found in the series *The World of 5G*, which consists of five volumes.

The volume *The World of 5G: Internet of Everything* is edited by Xue Quan, Director of Guangdong Key Laboratory of Millimeter Wave and Terahertz, South China University of Technology, and mainly expounds the iterative development history of mobile communication technology, the characteristics and limitations of the first four generations of mobile communication technology, the technical characteristics of 5G and its possible industrial application prospects, and the development trend of mobile communication technology in the post-5G era. By reading this volume, the reader can obtain a carefully and skillfully drawn picture of the past, present, and future applications of 5G.

The volume *The World of 5G: Intelligent Manufacturing* is edited by Dr. Guo Jishun of Automotive Engineering Research Institute of Guangzhou Automobile Group Co., Ltd., and mainly introduces the development process of the Industrial Revolution, the opportunity brought about by 5G to the manufacturing industry, the upgrade of smart creation assisted by 5G, and the application of intelligent production based on 5G. Through this volume, readers can understand the opportunities for the transformation of traditional manufacturing produced by 5G+ smart creation and learn by experience what kind of revolution manufacturing innovation will create in the society.

The volume *The World of 5G: Intelligent Home* is edited by Wu Wei from Skyworth Group Co., Ltd., and mainly elaborates on the evolution of smart home, the key technologies that 5G uses to facilitate the intelligent development of home life, as well as innovative smart home products based on 5G technology. Home furnishing is closely tied to our daily life. By reading this volume, readers can understand the convenience and comfort arising from the integration of 5G and smart home. It provides a glimpse of the wonderful life that technology has created.

The volume *The World of 5G: Intelligent Transportation* is edited by Xu Zhiqiang from Guangzhou Hexin Communications Technology Co., Ltd., and mainly describes the development process of smart transportation, the key 5G technologies and architectures used in smart transportation, as well as the application examples of smart transportation based on 5G. By reading this volume, readers can be fully informed about the future development trend of smart transportation led by 5G technology.

The volume *The Word of 5G: Intelligent Medicine* is edited by Huang Wenhua and Lin Haibin from Southern Medical University, and mainly focuses on the effect of the integration of 5G and medical treatment, including the advantages of smart medicine compared with traditional medical treatment, how 5G promotes the development of smart medicine and smart medicine terminals and new medical applications integrated with 5G. Reading between the lines, readers can gain a comprehensive understanding of the huge application potential of 5G technology in the medical industry and be keenly aware of the well-being that technological progress has contributed to human health.

Finally, we specially acknowledge the funding from projects such as prior research and development projects "Key Technology of Millimeter Wave Integrated RF Front-end System Compatible with C Band (2018YFB1802000)" of the National Ministry of Science and Technology, the major science and technology project of "Research on 5G Millimeter Wave Broadband High Efficiency Chip and Phased Array System (2018B010115001)" of Guangdong Science and Technology Department, and Strategic Consulting Project of "Guangdong New Generation Information Technology Development Strategy Research (201816611292)" of Guangdong Research Institute of Chinese Academy of Engineering Development Strategy.

5G brings us technological change, industry upgrade, and social upheaval with unprecedented speed and strength, while also generating great challenges. Let's navigate our way ahead while harnessing the waves of 5G.

About the Authors

Quan Xue (M'02–SM'04–F'11) received his B.S., M.S., and Ph.D. degrees in electronic engineering from the University of Electronic Science and Technology of China (UESTC), Chengdu, China, in 1988, 1991, and 1993, respectively. In 1993, he joined the UESTC as a Lecturer. He became a Professor in 1997. From October 1997 to October 1998, he was a Research Associate and then a Research Fellow with the Chinese University of Hong Kong. In 1999, he joined the City University of Hong Kong and was a Chair Professor of Microwave Engineering. He also served the University as the Associate Vice President, the Director of Information and Communication Technology Center, and the Deputy Director of the State Key Lab of Millimeter Waves (Hong Kong). In 2017, he joined the South China University of Technology where now he is a Professor and also serves as the Dean of the School of Electronic and Information Engineering, the Dean of the School of Microelectronics, the Director of the Guangdong Key Laboratory of Terahertz and Millimeter Waves.

He has authored or co-authored over 400 internationally refereed journal papers and over 150 international conference papers. He is the co-inventor of more than 20 granted Chinese patents and more than 30 granted US patents, five of which have been transferred. His research interests include microwave/millimeter-wave/THz passive components, active components, antenna, microwave monolithic integrated circuits

(MMIC, and radio frequency integrated circuits (RFIC), etc. Professor Xue is a Fellow of IEEE. He served the IEEE as an AdCom member of MTT-S (2011–2013) and the Associate Editor of *IEEE Transactions on Microwave Theory and Techniques* (2010–2013), the Editor of *International Journal of Antennas and Propagation* (2010–2013), the Associate Editor of *IEEE Transactions on Industrial Electronics* (2010–2015), the Associate Editor of *IEEE Transactions on Antenna and Propagations* (2016). Professor Xue is the winner of the 2017 H. A. Wheeler Applications Prize Paper Award.

Wenquan Che received her B.Sc. degree from the East China Institute of Science and Technology, Nanjing, China, in 1990, her M.Sc. degree from the Nanjing University of Science and Technology (NUST), Nanjing, China, in 1995, and her Ph.D. degree from the City University of Hong Kong (CITYU), Kowloon, Hong Kong, in 2003.

In 1999, she was a Research Assistant with the City University of Hong Kong. In 2002, she was a Visiting Scholar with the Polytechnique de Montréal, Montréal, QC, Canada. She has been with NUST during 1995–2018 as Lecturer, Associate Professor and then Full Professor. She had been the Executive Dean of Elite Education College of NUST during 2013–2018. She is now a Full Professor with the South China University of Technology. From 2007 to 2008, she conducted academic research with the Institute of High Frequency Technology, Technische Universität München, Munich, Germany. During 2005–2006 and 2009–2016, she was with the City University of Hong Kong as a Research Fellow and a Visiting Professor. She has authored or co-authored over 300 internationally refereed journal papers and over 200 international conference papers. Her current research interests include microwave and millimeter-wave circuits and systems, microwave monolithic integrated circuits, antenna technologies, and the medical applications of microwave technologies.

Dr. Che is currently an Elected Member of the IEEE MTT-S AdCom (2018–2023) and the Editor-in-Chief of Microwave and Optical Technology Letters (2019–2022). She was a recipient of the 2007 Humboldt Research Fellowship presented by the Alexander von Humboldt Foundation of Germany, the 5th China Young Female Scientists Award in 2008, and also the Distinguished Young Scientist awarded by the National Natural Science Foundation Committee of China in 2012. She has been a reviewer for IET Microwaves, Antennas and Propagation. She is now an Associate Editor of *IEEE Journal of Electromagnetics, RF, and Microwaves in Medicine and Biology*, and Reviewer for *IEEE Transactions on Microwave Theory and Techniques*, *IEEE Transactions on Antennas and Propagation*, *IEEE Transactions on Industrial Electronics*, and *IEEE Microwave and Wireless Components Letters*.

Contents

Chapter 1

Progress of Civilization with Information: The Never-Ending Human Quest

1.1 The Evolution of Transmission Mode for Human Information

The evolution of human civilization is, in essence, a history of information recording and transmission, a history which witnessed the gradual increase in information storage capacity and continuous improvements in transmission speed and width. The ability to obtain information is the fundamental power to change humanity. In the theory of the origin of humans, why did apes eventually evolve into humans? This is largely because of the difference in the communication ability between apes and other animals. Looking back at history, it can be seen that the speed of development of human society is almost directly proportional to that of information transmission. From language, writing, radio to the Internet, information storage is getting bigger and bigger, the speed of information transmission is getting faster and faster, and the human society is also getting more and more advanced, marching forward full of hope. With the continuous progress in information transmission, mankind has stepped into a brilliant process of scientific and technological development, and continuous development of society, and human being has become a real "intelligent creature" on the blue Earth. The following section provides a quick review of how human information transmission has evolved and transitioned over the years.

1.1.1 *Language: The key to human domination on Earth*

Apart from crawling, walking upright, and learning to make tools, what was the most important achievement of the apes in their evolution? It is the formation of language. It is no exaggeration to say that language has made human beings and thus human society. Compared to animals' speech center, the language formed by human beings during the evolution possesses unique social attributes and complex systematic properties, which display the fundamental difference between human language and animal language, thus making human beings the world's dominant players eventually.

The most important function of language is information exchange. The emergence of language ushered in the first information revolution, and thus, the human society driven by information sharing was constructed. With the help of language, human beings can realize the synchronous transmission of information face to face. They can also spread information to different regions in the dimension of space or pass it on from generation to generation in the dimension of time through oral transmission. However, owing to the limitations in memory and communication efficiency, communication content and communication population are also limited.

1.1.2 *Word or character: The carrier for creating and inheriting human civilization*

With the progress of human beings and the development of society, the requirements for information storage gradually came into force. Language information is unstable, and the transmission of language alone will cause miscommunication, and the information cannot be stored reliably, so it is difficult to establish a lasting and systematic information transmission method. Before the invention of written language, human beings relied on tying ropes to preserve some information. Besides the small amount of information storage, this method also had other limitations which made it impossible for it to become an effective carrier of information.

The emergence of written language enables the human society to effectively store and disseminate information, thus creating a human civilization that can be passed down from generation to generation. The use of written language enabled more reliable recording and transmission than verbal communication alone, triggering a second information revolution.

The long, traceable history of mankind owes much to the carrier of words, which can preserve information and spread it across time and space.

1.1.3 *Radio-by-air communication reaching thousands of miles*

From word of mouth and beacon alarm to letters transmitted by courier stations and books containing human wisdom as well as thoughts, the speed of information transmission has gradually accelerated, its space has gradually expanded, and the number of people involved has also gradually increased. However, both sending mail and publishing books have time limitations, which may take several days or even months. With the continuous progress of human society, such a delay will make it difficult to meet people's urgent requirements for the speed of information transmission. Therefore, radio, which changed the history of human information transmission, came to the fore. In the 18th century, with the painstaking efforts of scientists, like Franklin and Volt, human beings started their research on electricity. Thanks to the contributions of Faraday, Hertz, Maxwell, and other scientists, the theory of electromagnetism was perfected and matured, which laid a solid foundation for the emergence of radio. Tesla, Popov, and Marconi all contributed significantly to the creation and invention of the radio. In 1901, Marconi completed a 3600 km transatlantic radio communication, heralding a new information revolution. On the basis of telegrams, new information transmission methods, such as telephone and radio, came into being one after another.

Printing allows words to be transmitted through books, but not in real time. The use of radiotelephones and radio stations allows speech to break through the limitations of space and carry on real-time transmission over a long distance, which is a major change in the history of human information transmission. Later, as an important carrier of multimedia, television (known as the carrier of the fourth information revolution) came into being. This way of information transmission became more popular and had more impact, with television becoming one of the harbingers of modern civilization. The advent of television has greatly enriched the spiritual and cultural lives of human beings, but it is a one-way information transmission. With the passing of time, the existing information transmission mode can no longer meet the growing individualized requirements, and it puts forward higher requirements for the information revolution again.

This time, a more powerful type of Internet has stepped onto the historical stage.

1.1.4 *The Internet: Efficient sharing regardless of the distance*

In order to satisfy people's desire for faster and real-time communication, especially the higher requirements for two-way communication of information, the Internet emerged. The Internet has brought information dissemination to new heights in the history of the information revolution. The Internet effectively merges all the features of previous information carriers such as real-time transmission, remote usage, and multimedia, and digitization offers unprecedented flexibility to information transmission. Using the Internet, people can receive and transmit information anytime and anywhere. At the same time, owing to the advantage of mass storage of the Internet, people are exposed to a wider world of information.

The Internet, which originated in the 1960s, was initially a military network built by the United States and the Soviet Union during the Cold War to connect several computers. After that, the email that could communicate between hosts came out, and network communication became efficient and fast. In the 1980s, with the emergence of Wide Area Network (WAN), more and more people began to use the Internet as a tool for information communication. In the 1990s, with the emergence of browser and web technology, the Internet ushered in an era of development with high speed. In 1995, the National Science Foundation Network of the United States (NSFNET) was officially launched for commercial use, and the Internet began to sweep the world. Compared to previous information transmission methods, the speed, real-time and non-real-time compatibility, richness of the content, and the breadth of dissemination of information on the Internet are all unprecedented. With the help of the Internet, the amount and speed of information transmission have reached unprecedented levels. With the help of the Internet, all kinds of information can be exchanged efficiently, thus greatly improving the efficiency of human life and production activities, and directly resulting in the rapid progress of productivity and production relations.

As seen from the changes and transition of several ways of information transmission summarized in Fig. 1.1, we can find that language played a very important role in the evolution of apes in that it separated

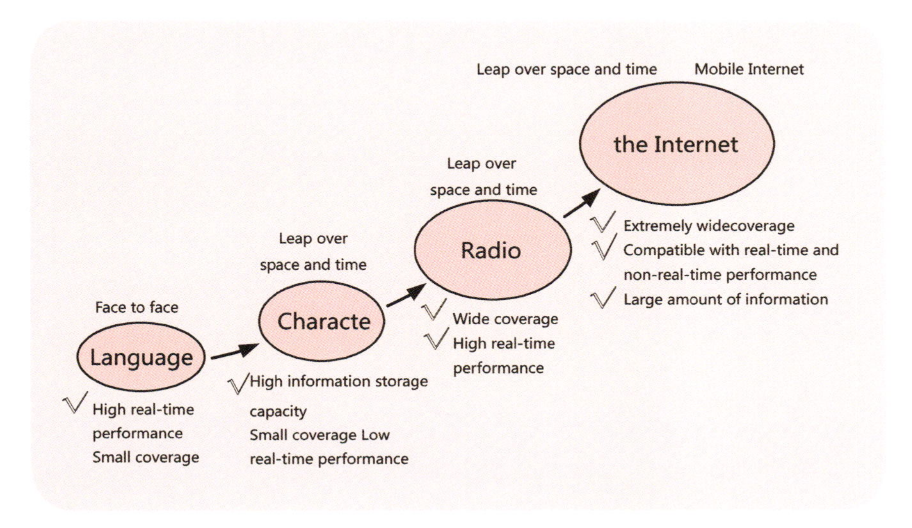

Figure 1.1 Changes in the way of human information dissemination.

them from other animals. Language is the only means of information transmission and is even considered the symbol of the beginning of human civilization. Since then, the means of information transmission have become more advanced with the spread of information farther and farther, also reaching larger and larger groups of people. Human beings are like dancers in magic shoes, spinning faster and faster, with something to rejoice in and be proud of. The following is a brief introduction to the mobile communication technology that has had a profound impact on information transmission in the human society since the 1980s.

1.2 The Iterative Process of Fourth-Generation (4G) Mobile Communication

Following the invention of the telegraph and telephone and the discovery of electromagnetic waves, the way people communicate has gone through earthshaking changes in the mid- and late-19th century. The "clairvoyant" and "wind-drift ear" in fairy tales are no longer fanciful, yet the ink-writing days when the cars, horses, and mail were all very slow also gradually faded away because mobile communication has been updated several times till now. We usually use 1G to 5G to classify the stages of mobile communication history. In the 1G era, information transmission was inefficient, taking the form of analog voice. The mobile terminal was a big and bulky "mobile phone", and Motorola was the popular "star" in the 1G era. In the 2G era, with the development of digital signal technology, the information was transmitted wirelessly with voice calls and text messages after digitalization. The Global System for Mobile Communications (GSM) standard became dominant in the 2G era, and communication tools by Ericsson, Nokia, and other brands became dominant in the field of base stations and terminals. In the 3G era, WCDMA [Wideband Code Division Multiple Access (CDMA)] and CDMA 2000 have gradually evolved into two major standards. At the same time, the transmission of more text and image information began to be popularized, and mobile terminals showed a trend of being lightweight and intelligent. At this stage, the most popular mobile phone brands were Apple, Samsung, and so on. In the 4G era, the Long-Term Evolution (LTE) standard has been mainstreamed in the wireless communication industry. Multimedia technologies such as Internet access, video, and instant messaging have developed rapidly, enriching people's lives. The disappearance of physical keyboards and the expansion of screen size have doubled the user experience, making Huawei one of the leaders in communication. In Fig. 1.2, we can see the changes in mobile communication terminal in

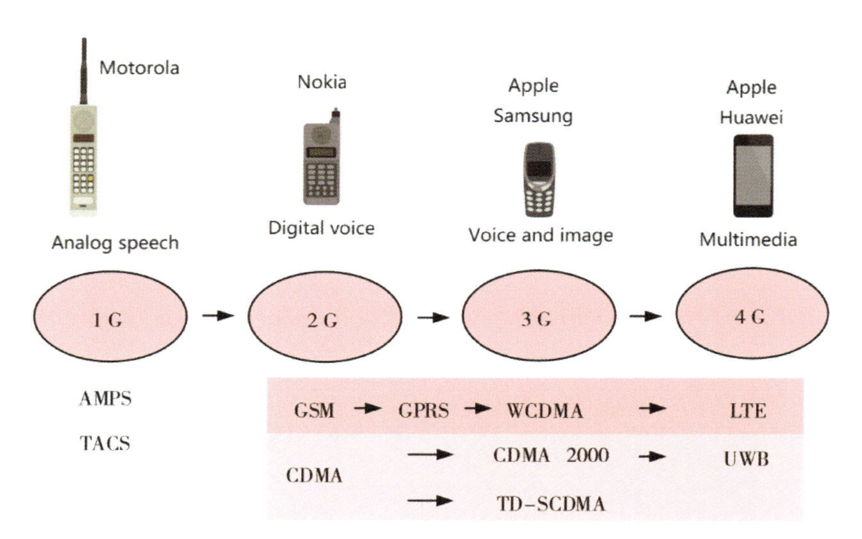

Figure 1.2 The iterative course of the fourth generation of mobile communication terminals.

the iterative process more intuitively. If road traffic is used to figuratively describe the change from 1G to 4G, then it is like a development from narrow country roads to wide and flat highways. The onset of 5G application, however, is more than just the broadening of roads. It is more like the fusion of high-speed air, sea, and land routes and even interstellar routes. As it is important to know the reason why it happened, the iterative history of 4G mobile communications has been inevitably included to describe the revolutionary impact that 5G's arrival has had on people's lives.

1.2.1 *The first-generation (1G) mobile communication: The winding narrow country roads*

Figure 1.3 helps us gain a general understanding of the developments during the first generation of mobile communication. 1G mobile communication is a cellular wireless telephone system based on analog technology and Frequency Division Multiple Access (FDMA) technology, mainly providing analog voice services. The first generation of mobile communication realizes multi-user access by modulating and transmitting multichannel signals with different carrier frequencies. The core network adopts the public switched telephone network (PSTN) based on simulation technology with the peak value for theoretical transmission speed of only 2 Kb/s.

1.2.1.1 *The developments*

Let's go back to the World's Fair in 1939. It was at this conference that AT&T, the then largest telecommunications operator in the United States,

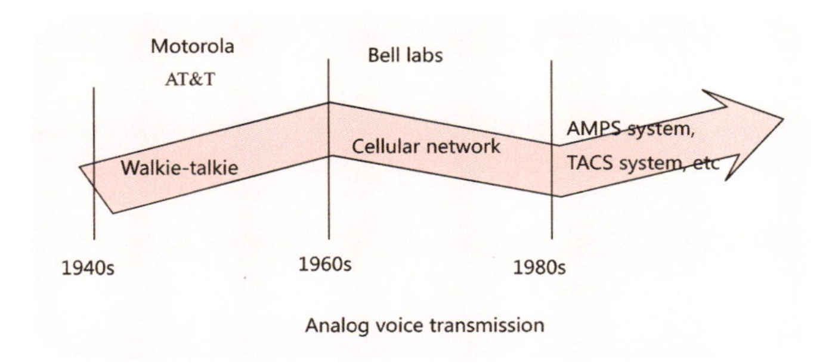

Figure 1.3 Development of the first generation of mobile communication.

put forward the concept of the first generation of mobile communications. But the idea was rejected by the Federal Communications Commission (FCC) because the technology was limited at the time and there was no proper allocation of spectrum for mobile technology. It wasn't until 1969, 30 years later, when cable began to be employed for television and has been prevailing till date, that the FCC allocated the spectrum for mobile communication, as many stations retreated from the spectrum used to carry television signals. Therefore, the 1G era came into being only after another 30 years and a thousand entreaties.

Actually, in the few decades AT&T has been waiting for this, mobile communications have left their marks on history. For example, Motorola produced its first walkie-talkie SCR-536 in the 1940s, and AT&T developed the Mobile Telephone Service (MTS) and the Improved Mobile Telephone Service (IMTS) in the 1940s and 1960s. In the 1980s, pagers began to enter the life of Chinese people. We call these technologies applied in mobile communication 0G mobile communication, which represents the pre-mobile communication era. But by this time, the terminals were either ridiculously bulky, like walkie-talkies, weighing tens of kilograms, and requiring special signalmen to carry them during World War II. In addition, it doesn't have a direct voice transmission function, like a pager, and you'll have to find another phone to call back after you receive the message.

In the 1960s, Bell Labs proposed the concept of a cellular communication network, as shown in Fig. 1.4. The cellular network with a hexagonal shape can be used to divide the mobile communication area into nearly cellular units, each of which is covered by the corresponding base station. Inside the cellular communication network, adjacent units communicate at different frequencies to avoid mutual interference. Two non-adjacent units can, respectively, use the same frequency communication, so as to realize frequency reuse, improve users' access to the communication system, and provide technical support for the growth of the first generation of mobile communication in the 1970s and the realization of commercial use in the 1980s.

In 1978, AT&T introduced the Advanced Mobile Phone System (AMPS), the representative standard of the 1G era, based on the cellular communication network. The system operates at 800 MHz and 900 MHz, and is mainly widely used in North and South America and parts of the Pacific Rim. Bell Labs also launched the system in Chicago in the same year and had a successful trial run, but at that time, the AMPS had not yet been formally deployed for commercial use in the United States.

Figure 1.4 Cellular communication network model.

In 1979, Japan introduced its first mobile communication standard, Nippon Telegraph and Telephone system (NTT), which operated at 450 MHz and 800 MHz. Later, it was developed into HICAP (High-Capacity Version of NTT), an upgraded version of NTT.

In 1981, Sweden established the Nordic Mobile Telephone (NMT) system with working frequency bands of 450 MHz and 900 MHz, which were applied in some Nordic and Eastern European countries and Russia and other regions. It was also the year that the United States finally began to officially deploy AMPS commercial operations.

In 1985, the UK introduced the Total Access Communications System (TACS) based on AMPS. The main operating frequency band of the system was 900 MHz and this was widely used in Britain, Japan, and some Asian countries. In the same year, Radiocom 2000 for France, RTMS for Italy, and C-450 for Germany and Southern Africa were all deployed. So, the first two standard operating frequency bands were 450 MHz and 900 MHz, respectively, and the last one was 450 MHz.

On November 18, 1987, the first generation analog mobile communication system in China was officially launched and commercialized in Guangdong, adopting the TACS standard. The theoretical transfer rate of this system was only 2.4 Kb/s, with only 700 initial users.

The diverse standards mentioned above mainly are "national standards" rather than "international standards". There was also no common interface between the different standards, which made roaming, or cross-country communication, impossible. During this period, the European countries operated independently. Although many standards were opened, they were not widely used, which led to the dominance of the United States in the 1G era. As a result, AMPS operated in more than 72 countries and territories until February 18, 2008, when operators in the United States ceased to operate AMPS. TACS, the European regional standard, is only used in about 30 countries. Our country closed the operation of this system on December 31, 2001.

Compared to the diverse and different standards, the research and development of the mobile communication terminal appears to be relatively simple. While AT&T advanced and improved AMPS, Motorola, an American communications giant, was committed to the development of mobile phones. In 1973, Martin Cooper's team first developed "Big Phone", which later became popular all over the world, supporting AMPS, TACS, NMT, and other standards. The strong portability of the "mobile phone" arising from its size, much smaller than that of the previous walkie-talkie, resulted in the onset of the use of mobile communication use by the whole population. As such, Motorola has become the crown king in the era of analog communication.

1.2.1.2 *Weakness or deficiency*

(1) *Single business type*: During this period, on the one hand, mobile communication services only supported analog voice transmission with limited types of services. Moreover, standards were mixed, and there was no common interface between them, which made roaming impossible for communication. On the other hand, limited by transmission bandwidth, only regional mobile communication could be realized in the 1G era.

(2) *Limited number of simultaneous access users*: It is well known that frequency resources were very limited. In the 1G era, FDMA technology was adopted, and each mobile communication user had to occupy a channel separately when talking. When a certain channel frequency of the base station is occupied by someone, other users cannot communicate at this frequency. Even if the cellular communication network was divided into multiple space–time frequencies, the number

of users connected to a system at the same time was still very limited with a low-frequency utilization rate.

(3) *Poor communication quality*: Mobile communication in the 1G era was mainly analog communication. It was impossible to compress, encrypt, or add calibration to the transmitted signal. Therefore, mobile communication in this period had the common phenomena of serial number, stealing listening and stealing number, with its low efficiency of the frequency spectrum and weak anti-interference ability. All in all, poor communication quality meant poor and low confidentiality.

(4) *Bulky mobile communication terminals*: The transmission of analog signals required the continuous conversion of voice signals and electrical signals between the transceiver and the receiver, which in turn required good system capacity and battery life of the equipment. Limited by the battery manufacturing technology, integrated circuit technology, and antenna size, the equipment in that time was large and expensive. During the 1980s in China, the market price of a "mobile phone" was as high as tens of thousands of yuan, and it became a symbol of status.

The inherent inadequacies of the first generation of mobile communications so doomed that they could not "fly into the home". Finally, with the dawn of the digital mobile communication era, namely the 2G era, 1G gradually disappeared.

1.2.2 *The second-generation (2G) mobile communication: An easily accessible thoroughfare to ride galloping horses*

The second generation of mobile communication mainly features digital communication and adopts two technologies: time division multiple access (TDMA) and CDMA. Pre-emptively, Ericsson and Nokia proposed the GSM standard based on TDMA technology and became the representative enterprises in the 2G era. When Qualcomm proposed the CDMA standard again, half of the mobile communication market had already been occupied by others. It is regrettable that Motorola, a dominant company with which other companies found it difficult to compete in the analog communication era, failed to keep up with the tide because of its slow transformation, leading to it finally disappearing in history.

1.2.2.1 *The developments*

From the late 1980s to the early 1990s, with the maturity of digital signal processing, large-scale integrated circuit, microprocessor, and other technologies, the second generation of mobile communication system came into force, and people entered the era of digital mobile communication. Digital circuit is not only more stable but also more integrated than analog circuit. A dedicated chip has replaced hundreds of chips in the past, greatly reducing the size of terminal devices and making them more affordable. It was at this time that the "mobile phone" gradually became a household word.

Figure 1.5 shows the main development process in the 2G era. The communication standards in this period were divided into two categories: one is based on TDMA and represented by GSM, including IDEN (Integrated Digital Enhanced Network), D-AMPS (Digital AMPS), and PDC (Personal Digital Cellular Communication System); the other is based on CDMA, typically represented by IS-95 (or cdmaOne). Although the mainstream service positioning in the 2G era was the digital cellular voice service, the low-speed data service had begun to develop. For example, mobile phones can send short messages, browse the Web at a slow speed under the Symbian system, or use QQ and MSN to chat. Core networks in the 2G era continue to follow the previous PSTN foundation. Channel coding adopts turbo codes close to the Shannon limit, and digital modulation methods such as Gaussian minimum shift keying (GMSK), 8 phase shift keying (8PSK), and 16 quadrature amplitude modulation (16QAM) are also adopted. It can provide a transfer rate of 9.6–28.8 Kb/s.

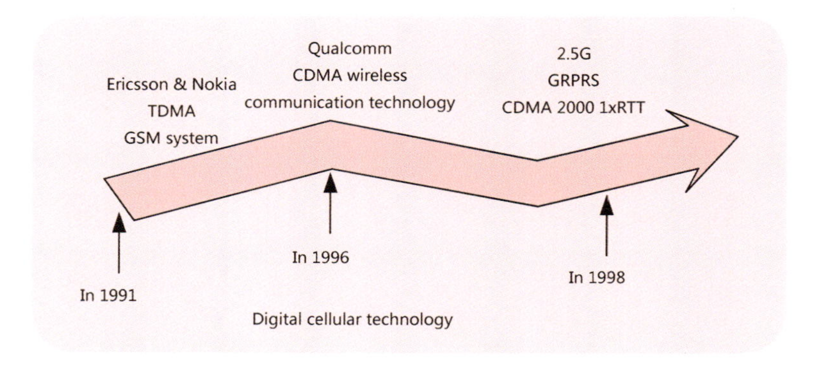

Figure 1.5 Development of the second generation of mobile communication.

In the course of the development of mobile communication, a new generation of communication standard will appear every 10 years. Those who master the standards will have the right to speak in the industry, which is the embodiment of the soft power of countries and enterprises. Different from the 1G era, when all the princes rose up and the vassals quarreled, the standard made for 2G showcased the state of "sticking together".

In 1983, to get ahead of the game, several European countries formed the GSM (short for Groupe Spécial Mobile committee) to study the standards for digital cellular voice communications.

In 1991, Ericsson and Nokia launched the first GSM system in Europe and at the same time signed the Memorandum of Understanding (MoU) for the system design of a registered trademark. The GSM was renamed as the Global System for Mobile Communications, commonly known as "Global". This officially marked the entry of people into the era of the second-generation mobile communication. GSM was developed to allow users to use the same mobile standard globally, allowing them to travel around the world with a single phone. Its core technology was TDMA, which divides a single wireless channel into eight time slots for multiple users to take turns to use, thus realizing channel sharing and improving user capacity. In the same year, the first batch of 300 Subscriber Identity Module (SIM) cards in history was shipped from Giesecke & Devrient GmbH (G&D) in Munich, Germany, to Radiolinja, a wireless network operator in Finland, for access to the 2G network. Japan's communications standard, the PDC, was also introduced in this year.

In 1993, China's first GSM network opened in Jiaxing, Zhejiang province, thus marking the official beginning of 2G era in China.

By October 1994, there have already been 50 GSM systems in operation worldwide, with a total userbase of more than 4 million, the calling number of the international roaming users of more than 5 million per month, and an average growth of over 50% in the number of users. Therefore, 2G networks were being deployed in full swing around the world.

In 1996, the China Telecom GSM had more than 30 global roaming partners, the momentum of development being unstoppable.

At this point, people might wonder what the United States, the leader of the 1G era, has been doing. The United States introduced its digital standard in 1990, IS-54 or D-AMPS, which was also based on TDMA technology, but perhaps it was caught up too much in the halo of the

1G analog era to pay much attention to this revolutionary change. In December 1992, Germany had a GSM penetration rate of 71%, compared to a 2G penetration rate of 0.1% in the US. By the time Qualcomm's CDMA-based IS-95 became the 2G standard, the technology of GSM had spread around the world and America had missed it. The results were clear: Nokia and Ericsson grew rapidly into the world's leading makers of telecom equipment and mobile phones during this period, while Motorola's share of the global mobile phone market, which had miscalculated the lifespan of the analog era, collapsed to 17% in 1997, and was kicked off its pedestal. But, the turnaround in Europe had been pretty good. At that time, China, as the world's largest mobile communication market, also adopted and supported the GSM standard, which was an important reason why the European GSM standard was able to successfully counter the attack. Although China did not participate in the formulation of standards or gain a share in the base station terminal industry during this period, the huge market increased the confidence of the government and enterprises to participate in the mobile communication industry, and they began to make efforts gradually and even took the lead in the global mobile communication standard formulation and equipment production in later development.

1.2.2.2 *Weakness or deficiency*

As shown in Fig. 1.6, compared to the first generation of mobile communications supported by the FDMA technology, the second generation of mobile communications employed TDMA and CDMA technology, using more encoded digital signal, high modulator, channel coding, interleaving, balanced, encryption, and voice coding technology. The above technologies

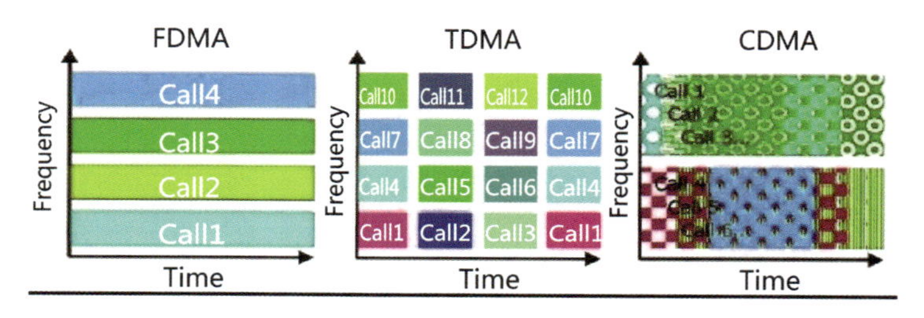

Figure 1.6 Comparison of the first and second generations of mobile communication coding technologies.

boosted the efficiency of the system spectrum, improved the system capacity and greatly enhanced voice quality and safety. At the same time, with the technologies of the second generation of mobile communications, roaming based on the SIM card can already be realized.

However, the second generation of mobile communication still had many shortcomings:

(1) *Limited types of data services*: During this period, the data transmission rate was low, mobile phones could only make calls, send text messages, and read e-books. But it was still difficult to surf the Internet, thus leading to the inability to meet the users' increasing demands for data transmission services.
(2) *Low coding quality*: The encoding speed of the GSM system is only 13 Kb/s, accounting for loud calls on GSM phones, which are not as good as those on wired phones.
(3) *TDMA technical limitations*: As shown in Fig. 1.6, with the rapid growth of the number of mobile communication users, the disadvantages of TDMA technology gradually emerge: misplacement and confusion of the time slot may lead to dropped calls. Simultaneously, TDMA's frequency allocation is complex, the synchronization overhead is much higher than CDMA, and the communication capacity is not as high as CDMA. As a result, when it came to the third generation of mobile communications, all the standards have chosen CDMA technology as the basis for development.

1.2.3 *The third generation (3G) mobile communication: Asphalt street to whisk*

Figure 1.7 provides a brief idea about the development course of the third generation of mobile communications. Communication technology in the 3G era was mainly characterized by high-speed data transmission technology and by high-quality digital communication, code division multiplexing, cellular system, turbo coding, dual polarization, and multi-band antenna, all of which promote the rapid development of mobile Internet. In the 3G era, Apple, Samsung, Qualcomm, and other companies rose rapidly, and China's wireless communication industry witnessed unsteadiness, while Nokia, the dominant mobile phone company in the 2G era, gradually disappeared.

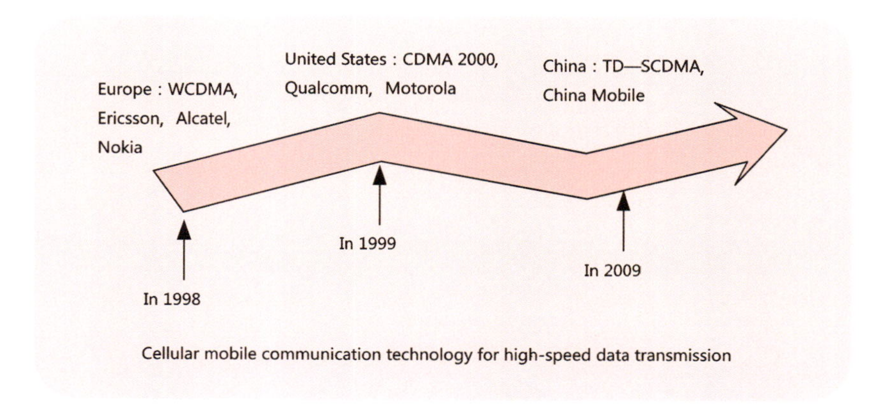

Figure 1.7 Development of the third generation of mobile communications.

1.2.3.1 *The developments*

2.5G, or second-generation semi-mobile communications, appeared amid the smooth transition from 2G to 3G. Provided the General Packet Radio Service (GPRS) based on the GSM system was introduced first, it could offer end-to-end wide area wireless IP connectivity. Network capacity was allocated only when required and was released when not needed, thus greatly raising the rate of communication transmission. The transmission rate of CDMA 2000 1xRTT (single-carrier radio transmission technology) could reach 144–384 Kb/s. Till now, we can still see GPRS or one capital letter "E" on the status bars on the cellphone, representing that the 2.5G signal is complementing the deficiency of 4G signals when the latter are poor. After the continuation by the 2.5G era, the third generation of mobile communication came into force trippingly. The Enhanced Data Rates for GSM Evolution (EDGE) is the highest wireless data transmission technology based on GSM before the emergence of 3G, which can provide broadband multimedia services through a wireless network and push the function of GPRS to its limit. In addition, the standard proposed in this period included CDMA 2000 1xRTT (single-carrier radio transmission technology) based on CDMA upon the standard with the transmission rate of 144–384 Kb/s. We still see GPRS, or a big "E", on the status bar of the phone when the 4G signal is terrible, indicating that the 2.5G signal is making up for the 4G shortfall. After the transition of the 2.5G era, the third generation of mobile communication has come into being.

In 1998, the International Telecommunication Union (ITU) asked for a global proposal for 3G wireless transmission, whose main requirements were high spectral efficiency and the ability to provide high-quality broadband and multimedia integrated services with global coverage. The third-generation mobile communications, International Mobile Telecommunications-2000 (IMT-2000) called as ITU, where "2000" refers to the operating frequency band of 2000 MHz, was known as the Universal Mobile Telecommunication System (UMTS) by European telecom giants. But the more commonly used acronym is 3G, referring to cellular mobile technology that supports high-speed data transmission. For its simple frequency planning, large system capacity, communication concealment and high confidentiality, good communication quality as well as other advantages, CAMA is favored by the 3G era. Three standards in this period are all formed based on the development of this technology.

In December 1998, Europe, Japan, and other countries and regions that originally promoted the GSM standard jointly established an organization to set up the global third-generation communication standard, which is the 3rd Generation Partnership Project (3GPP). The concept of wideband CDMA was first put forward by Japan, and WCDMA was finally developed after fusion and improvement. Benefiting from the high market share of GSM in the 2G era, WCDMA can be said to be born with a golden key and has the terminals with the most diversified 3G standards, occupying more than 80% of the global market share. Its backers include Europe's Ericsson, Alcatel, and Nokia, as well as manufacturers, such as Japan's NTT Docomo, Fujitsu, and Sharp.

In 1999, Japanese operator NTT Docomo introduced i-mode based on 2.5G networks, the world's first carrier-centric ecosystem. NTT Docomo cooperated with major websites to enable users to apply the i-mode button on their mobile phones to enjoy Internet services, such as sending emails, reading news, listening to music, and shopping online. The success of i-mode confirmed the viability of the 3G business model and gave a big boost to Japan's 3G network while also strengthening the determination of European operators to build 3G services. Unfortunately, the i-mode failed to go out of Japan and ended during the 4G era.

Immediately after that, the United States, unwilling to lag behind, led the launch of 3rd Generation Partnership Project 2 (3GPP2) to compete with 3GPP in January 1999, which was dominated by Qualcomm with the participation of Motorola, Lucent, and Samsung. Based on the previous

IS-95, CDMA 2000 was developed, which can be directly upgraded from the previous cdmaOne structure to 3G with low cost. But the application areas included only Japan, South Korea, and North America, so the supporters were not as many as that of WCDMA.

In response to Code Division Multiple Access (CDMA), the Synchronous Code Division Multiple Access (SCDMA) is set up by the Original Telecommunication Science and Technology Research Institute (later Datang Telecom) with the support of the Ministry of Telecommunications Industry. Time Division-Synchronous Code Division Multiple Access (TD-SCDMA) is the synchronous code division multiple access (TDMA) standard researched and drafted based on the TD technology of Siemens in Germany. Since then, China has competed for global communication standard making.

In order to implement real-time duplexing (also known as duplexing) in mobile communication, two schemes are generally adopted: one is Frequency Division Duplexing (FDD), in which uplink and downlink use different frequencies for transmission; the other is Time Division Duplexing (TDD), which uses the same frequency to divide the time slots for the incoming and outgoing signals. The advantage of FDD is that it allocates a separate frequency for the incoming and outgoing signals, with high transceiver efficiency and high frequency resource occupancy. TDD uses the division of time slots. The repeated use of frequency makes the transmission efficiency of TDD not as high as that of FDD. However, if the signal transmission speed is fast enough, TDD can also achieve higher transceiver efficiency. TD-SCDMA is the first standard to use TDD technology in the history of communication. FDD technology has always been used before. In addition, TD-SCDMA is known as "green 3G" due to its low radiation and is suitable for upgrading GSM system to 3G without the intermediate link of 2.5G. Compared to the other two 3G standards, which are CDMA 2000 and WCDMA, TD-SCDMA has a late start, as a result its technology is not mature enough.

In May 2000, the ITU officially announced the 3G mobile communication standard. TD-SCDMA, which owns the Chinese independent intellectual property rights, WCDMA in Europe, and CDMA 2000 in the United States jointly became the international standard in the 3G era, forming a tripartite confrontation situation.

In January 2009, enactment of the three 3G licenses in China marked Chinese's formal entry into the 3G era. Among them, China Mobile obtained TD-SCDMA, China Unicom and China Telecom WCDMA and CDMA 2000.

Communication standards during this period used CDMA, 32QAM digital modulation, and turbo channel coding. The core network was divided into circuit switching (CS) domain and packet switching (PS) domain, which provided "circuit service" and "packet data service" for users, respectively. The information rate of 3G mobile communication achieved the transmission of variable bit rate information according to the bandwidth requirements, which can reach 144 Kb/s in the case of high-speed movement, 384 Kb/s in the case of walking movement, and 2 Mb/s in the case of indoor movement, making a huge leap compared to the 2G era. It has enabled high-quality digital communications, made mobile Internet a reality and ushered in the "age of pictures". Since then, network data service has become the main function ahead of making phone calls, and then the smartphone came into being.

In 1997, Microsoft released the first smartphone operating system, Windows CE, for a limited hardware environment. However, for lack of practical experience on mobile terminals, Windows CE not only runs slowly but also fills the small screen of mobile phones with Start menu and task bar in the style of Microsoft desktop system. The interface is not simple enough, and the font is also difficult to read.

In 1998, Pison, Nokia, Ericsson, and Motorola created Symbian as a joint venture to compete with Microsoft's smartphone operating system. The development of the Symbian S40 and S60 systems provided most of the technical guidance for future smartphone systems.

In 2007, when Microsoft and Symbian were lopsided, Apple, which borrowed their technologies, released their first iPhone based on the iOS operating system. With its simple interface and touch screen technology, Apple stood out and became the leader of the smartphone market.

1.2.3.2 *Weakness or deficiency*

Despite its many advantages, 3G mobile communication technology still has the following disadvantages:

(1) Communication efficiency between the base stations is not high. In order to fit the characteristics of mobile communication in the 2G era, the end-to-end communication of mobile phones in the 3G era must go through several levels of forwarding. After the mobile phone signals are sent to the base station, they will be sent to the core network through the Baseband Unit (BBU) and Radio Network Controller (RNC) and then sent to the base station from the core network to RNC

and BBU, and finally the base station will communicate with the receiver. Therefore, the communication efficiency between base stations is not high.

(2) The data transmission rate cannot meet the requirements of users. Mobile phones in the 3G era can view pictures, browse the Web, and play games smoothly, but they still can't watch videos smoothly. Due to the limited bandwidth of 3G, there is a contradiction between transmission speed and anti-jamming capability.
(3) There is insufficient integration of the mobile communication network. Although the mobile communication network used for surfing the Internet and the original voice communication network in the 3G era can be integrated, they are independent of each other and are not unified with each other, resulting in unnecessary waste of resources.

These shortcomings of the third generation of mobile communications make it impossible to meet the requirements of users, so the mobile communication technology continues to improve, continues to move forward, and thus we usher in the 4G era.

1.2.4 *The fourth-generation (4G) mobile communication: Expressway for cars to run shoulder to shoulder*

Compared to the third-generation mobile communication technology, the fourth-generation mobile communication technology not only comprises faster transmission speed (about 20 times that of 3G) but also larger coverage range and capability to satisfy high-quality data service (images and video) with main characteristics of orthogonal frequency division multiplexing (OFDM), smart antenna and multiple input multiple output (MIMO), software radio, and multi-user detection, which realized the true application of high-speed mobile multimedia to meet almost all the requirements of wireless users and greatly change the way of life of human beings. Figure 1.8 allows the readers to quickly understand the development of the fourth generation of mobile communications. In the 4G era, the Chinese hardware manufacturer of communication equipment has made great progress, which aided the high-speed development of the mobile Internet era. It is characterized by fantastic payment methods through the mobile network (WeChat, Alipay), burgeoning of mobile end life service class O2O mode (Meituan, Eleme), the rapid emergence of

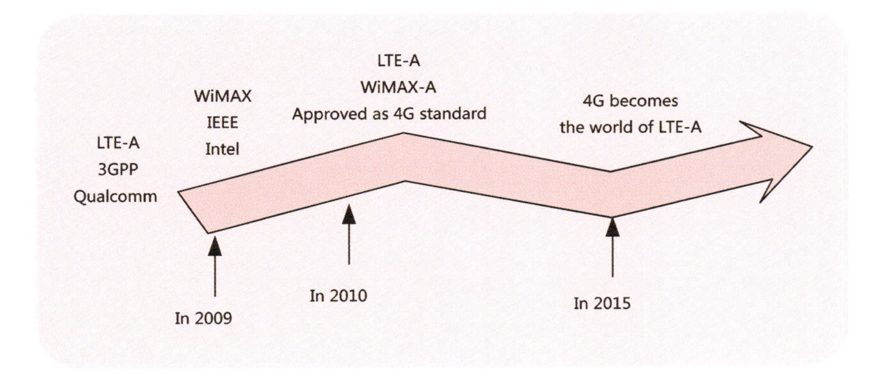

Figure 1.8 Development of the fourth generation of mobile communications.

Figure 1.9 Mobile Internet.

live and video service (bettas, trill, Bilibili, etc.) and increase in mobile end games (Netease game, Tencent), as shown in Fig. 1.9.

1.2.4.1 *The developments*

Although 3G introduced a transmission rate of up to 2 Mb/s, it still failed to meet the people's demand for mobile multimedia. Hence, mobile communication technology continued to develop. In 2002, 3GPP introduced High-Speed Downlink Packet Access (HSDPA) in the R5 version of WCDMA with increased data throughput through Adaptive Modulation and Coding (AMC) and Hybrid Automatic Repeat Request (HARQ) technologies. The specified downlink data transfer rate can reach up to 1.8 Mb/s. In 2004, WCDMA released Version R6 and introduced High-Speed Uplink Packet Access (HSUPA). Through multi-code transmission, HARQ, and fast scheduling based on Node B and other key technologies, the specified uplink packet data transmission rate can reach up to 2 Mb/s. The WCDMA version combining HSDPA and HSUPA is called High-Speed Packet Access (HSPA), which is considered to be the transition from 3G era to 4G era with the name of 3.5G era.

Technology is always evolving iteratively. In 2007, the R7 version of WCDMA was released to enhance HSPA, the so-called HSPA+. The downlink adopts 64QAM and MIMO technologies, and the uplink adopts 16QAM technology, which can provide the downlink peak data transmission rate of 28 Mb/s and the uplink peak data transmission rate of 11.5 Mb/s. HSPA+ was later listed by the ITU as one of the technical standards for the 4G era.

If 3G communication marks the era of mobile multimedia application for human beings, then 4G will lead human beings into the era of high-speed mobile multimedia. Across the city, "phubbers" can be seen using mobile Internet to watch TV dramas, movies, short videos, and live broadcasts. In fact, on the basis of 3G, 4G communication technology with the wireless local area network (WLAN) combined with "organic" realized the Ethernet access rate to provide users with integrated wireless wide area network and wireless local area network integration services, so as to ensure that mobile multimedia systems achieve high-quality images and video transmission. Different from the 3G dense cellular network, the 4G communication system adopts the worldwide unified digital IP cellular core network technology, which is an important milestone toward the intelligent development of the whole network.

As Qualcomm has a serious monopoly on CDMA technology in the 3G era, high licensing tax, Qualcomm tax, and reverse licensing have aroused the public's anger toward communication manufacturers. Therefore, in the 4G era, people choose to avoid CDMA when making communication standards and turn to OFDM technology instead.

In 1999, 802.11a Wi-Fi was introduced by the Institute of Electrical and Electronics Engineers (IEEE) as a wireless local area network standard based on OFDM technology, with a peak transmission rate of 54 Mb/s. Later, 802.11n, 802.11b, 802.16E, 802.11g, and other standards were successively introduced. Until 2005, Intel, IBM, Motorola,

Nokia, and Nortel invested nearly $4 billion in this field. They wanted to develop 802.16 into a 4G international communication standard. They called it Worldwide Interoperability for Microwave Access (WiMAX).

In February 2008, the Radio Communication Sector of the ITU officially issued a worldwide notice of its International Mobile Telecommunications-Advanced (IMT-Advanced) candidate technology. As of October 2009, a total of six technical proposals had been submitted by two international standardization organizations (3GPP and IEEE) and three countries (China, Japan, and South Korea).

In the ITU-R WP5D conference held in October 2010, 14 external review organizations evaluated the candidate technology solutions and finally determined that LTE-Advanced of 3GPP and 802.16m of IEEE were the international wireless communication standards of IMT-Advanced. Both of the two technology solutions include TDD and FDD modes. TD-LTE-Advanced technology guided by domestic manufacturers, which regarded Datang Mobile as the leading company, also passed all the evaluations at the same time and become one of the standard technologies of IMT-Advanced. 802.16m technical standard, also known as WiMAX-Advanced, is the second generation of WiMAX international standard after 802.16e, which is led by the WiMAX Forum.

WiMAX was also beloved by every aspect when it was first proposed and America declared it a game-changing technology. At the time, research papers on WiMAX were a blowout, and even Intel claimed that WiMAX chips cost a tenth as much as conventional 3G chips. Nortel, a Canadian firm, sold its traditional 3G business directly to Alcatel of France so as to concentrate on WiMAX. Japan, South Korea, and Taiwan followed WiMAX's steps. It was a picture of prosperity on every side. But China and Europe repeated the successful implementation of GSM in the 2G era by working together on LTE development, making WiMAX technology far less mature than LTE. Moreover, the problem of switching signals when mobile phones move from one WiMAX site to another makes WiMAX users' experience extremely poor.

By 2010, Intel, one of WiMAX's stalwarts, was the first to break up its WiMAX division. Since then, WiMAX technology was gradually abandoned by operators. Then, Nortel of Canada went bankrupt, and Clearwire of the United States, the world's largest WiMAX service provider, shifted its business focus from WiMAX to LTE-Advanced. In the end, LTE-Advanced technology standard became the mainstream standard in the 4G era, while WiMAX, which started aggressively, ended up as an experimental mouse.

On December 4, 2013, the formal issue of providing TDD-LTE 4G licenses to three major operators by the Ministry of Industry and Information Technology marked the official beginning of the 4G era in China. On February 27, 2015, the Ministry of Industry and Information Technology issued FDD-LTE licenses to China Telecom and China Unicom. On April 3, 2018, the Ministry of Industry and Information Technology issued a FDD-LTE license to China Mobile.

(1) *LTE-Advanced*: LTE, a standard formulated by 3GPP, is a technology system in the same line with GSM, GPRS, EDGE, WCDMA, and HSDPA.

In April 2008, 3GPP officially began research on LTE-Advanced and made a relevant time plan.

In October 2009, the 37 member units of 3GPP jointly submitted technical texts containing TDD and FDD to ITU and held two global seminars attended by independent reviewers to formally introduce LTE-Advanced to the world.

In June 2010, at the ITU-R WP5D conference in Da Nang, Vietnam, LTE-Advanced passed a performance assessment to meet all its technical requirements.

In October 2010, at the ITU-R WP5D conference held in Chongqing, the TDD technology of 3GPP LTE-Advanced proposed by the Chinese government passed the performance evaluation and officially became one of the technologies of IMT-Advanced.

In September 2011, 3GPP completed version R10, forming the initial version of the LTE-Advanced specification standard.

From September 2012 to December 2015, 3GPP completed the LTE-Advanced specification standard of R11–R13 in response to the increasing requirements for data service, among which R13 is the last forming specification standard of LTE-Advanced. Then, 3GPP began to study 5G requirements and key technologies.

(2) *WiMAX-Advanced (IEEE 802.16m)*: In 1999, the IEEE 802.16 working group was established to set up a global unified broadband wireless access standard and promote further development of broadband access technology.

WiMAX was proposed by the WiMAX Forum in June 2001. The standard formulation of IEEE 802.16-2004 for fixed mode and IEEE 802.16E-2005 for mobile mode was completed in June 2004 and December 2005, respectively.

In October 2009, the IEEE International Organization for Standardization and communications equipment companies such as Intel, Lucent, as well as Nortel jointly submitted the IMT-Advanced technical text based on 802.16m to ITU.

In April 2011, IEEE officially approved 802.16m as the next-generation WiMAX standard, which can support downlink data transmission rates of over 300 Mb/s.

In January 2012, the WiMAX specification was formally established as one of the 4G standards at the ITU plenary meeting.

1.2.4.2 *Challenges ahead*

4G mobile communication technology is confronted with the following challenges:

(1) *Safety*: In 4G communication networks, the system is more easily targeted due to an upsurge in the number of devices. In order to protect the data transmitted over the 4G network, multiple security protection mechanisms need to be established.
(2) *High IP device integration*: As voice and data networks converge, millions of new devices will be added to the 4G communication systems, requiring reprogramming of the entire Internet address space or allocating new address spaces to emerging wireless networks and existing networks.
(3) *User requirements*: With the emergence of 4G communication technology, people begin to feel the convenience brought about by high-speed data service to their life and work. Therefore, in the future, the mobile communication network will completely cover our office area, entertainment area, as well as residential area, and each scene will have completely different requirements for communication network. 4G network cannot meet the requirements of some scenarios with high mobility and high traffic density. In view of the new requirements of future users, more advanced mobile network communication technologies with higher speed should be explored.

1.2.5 *Our continued quest: Calling for new technology*

Since the 1980s, mobile communication technology has progressed apace. By now, the fifth generation of communication technology has gradually entered our lives. From the perspective of service form, it has significantly facilitated people's life and promoted the rapid development of the society. From the analog voice service digitized gradually to the multimedia technology supporting rapid voice, video, data, image transmission and other such service forms, all make people's lives more convenient while pushing society to evolve at a fast pace. In the foreseeable future, the transmission rate and communication capacity of mobile communication will be further improved, the 5G era is expected to emerge, and more functions and applications will enter the homes of the masses. Human development will enter a new era at an unprecedented speed.

Chapter 2

5G Roars: The Internet of Everything Comes True

5G technology is coming with a bang. Not only for mobile communication itself but also for other industries, the impact brought about by 5G will be profound. So, what is it about 5G that makes it so compelling compared to the first four generations of mobile technology? How can the dream of Internet of Everything be realized through 5G? In order to answer these questions, in this chapter, we provide a brief introduction to the background, spectrum, system architecture, and key technologies of 5G.

2.1 5G Background: The Fertile Soil for the Initial Efforts

2.1.1 *Standardization*

First, let's talk about the process of mobile communication standardization. In 1982, the European Telecommunications Standards Institute (ETSI) began to promote GSM standardization. Then, GSM won an overall market landslide, so standardization organizations such as ITU, 3GPP, and IEEE have been formed so far. In China, the China Communications Standards Association (CCSA) is mainly responsible for the formulation of Chinese standards, establishing a complete standardization system for the industry and striving to promote consensus among the stakeholders in aspects such as application, spectrum, and evolution technology, so as to ensure the long-term development of mobile communications.

There are profound technical and market reasons behind the evolution of mobile communication standards. Beginning with 3G, ITU identifies various inter-generation mobile communications with International Mobile Telecommunication (IMT). 3G, 4G, and 5G are, respectively, defined as IMT-2000, IMT-Advanced, and IMT-2020. It can be seen from Fig. 2.1(a) that in the evolution process from 3G to 4G, the availability of

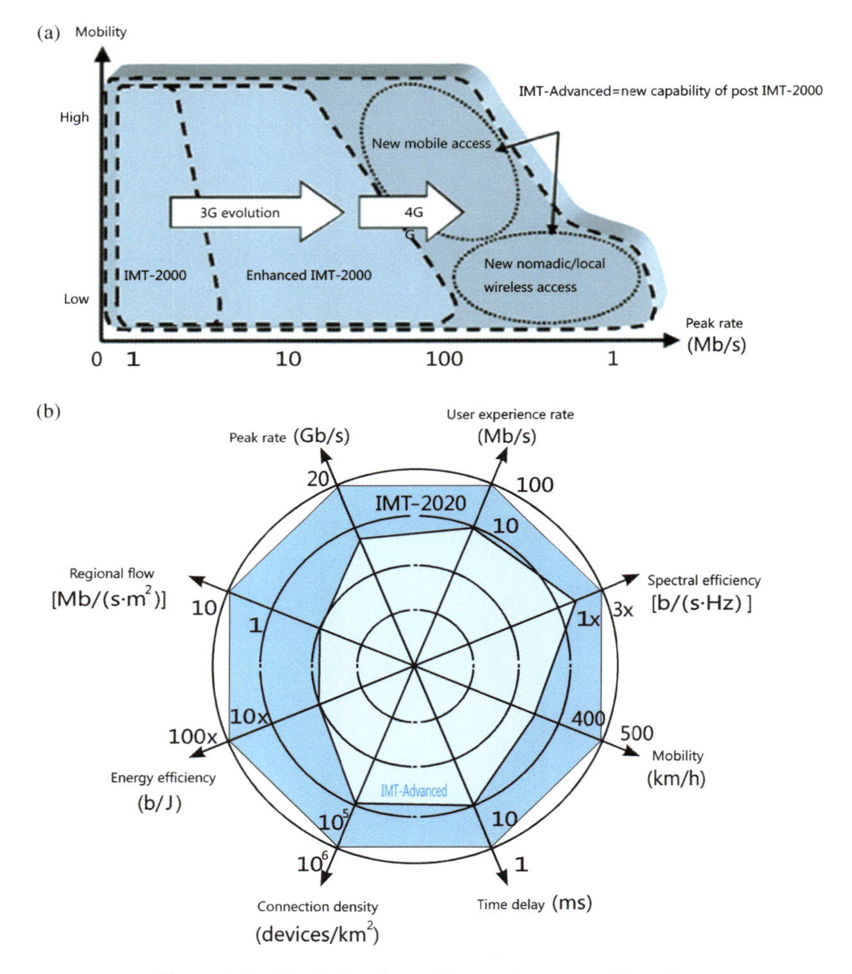

Figure 2.1 Evolution from 3G to 5G proposed by ITU.

the system is mainly reflected in two key indicators: peak rate and mobility. As shown in Fig. 2.1(b), during the evolution from 4G to 5G, the availability of the system further comprises eight performance indicators of mobile Internet and mobile Internet of Things. In the early stage of 3G standardization, voice mobile communication has become much more common. Moreover, video transmission is predicted to be the main driving force behind the development of mobile broadband. From the development trend of WeChat, TikTok, and Lark, it can be seen that the efforts made by standardization organizations are significantly forward-looking. Subsequently, the grouping of network businesses and the rapid growth of smartphones jointly propelled mobile communications from the era of voice and short messaging to the era of MBB (mobile broadband), the era of mobile Internet. In the era of mobile Internet, benefiting from the greatly reduced cost of end-to-end traffic and the rapid increase of the number of Internet users, 4G technology quickly promoted the wide use of mobile Internet applications such as social apps (WeChat, Weibo, TikTok, Facebook, Twitter, etc.), shopping apps (Jingdong, Taobao, Pinduoduo, Vipshop, Freshhema, Suning, etc.), municipal services apps (mobile tax, handheld provident fund, online government affairs, etc.), and mobile payment apps (Alipay, WeChat flash pay, Cloud flash pay, etc.). In the 5G era, MBB must be enhanced first, so enhanced mobile broadband (eMBB) is proposed. Next, based on the work of pushing NB-IoT by 3GPP in the 4G stage and the LTE-machine to machine (LTE-M) standardization, 5G will enhance the depth and breadth of mobile Internet of Things applications, realizing the rapid development of digitization for society, family, and industry.

3GPP occupies a core position in the 5G standardization process as the only organization with the capability of global mobile communication standards. The 5G standardization process is fair, open, and transparent. The reason lies in its leadership in technology inheritance, openness, inclusiveness, and technology protocol, which continuously promote the development and evolution of mobile communication. On the one hand, 5G inherits excellent mobile communication concepts, such as SIM cards enabling personal mobility and terminal mobility, Radio Access Network (RAN), and Core Network (CN) open interfaces. On the other hand, 5G also absorbs the essence of scientific and technological progress such as computing, control, and artificial intelligence and adjusts the service mode to meet the requirements of the public, enterprises, and industries. Take 3GPP's planned 5G Release 17 (a Release can be considered as a large and applicable version) as an example. Automatic network operation and maintenance will improve 5G network deployment and business provision capability through artificial intelligence; 5G will further enhance the capability of vertical industry application and drive the innovation of the whole industry and industrial chain through technological upgrading. 5G will achieve centimeter-level location tracking and improve the depth of coverage and mobility of the application.

In addition, the 3GPP absorbs the elements of 5.5G and 6G (IMT 2030), such as millimeter-wave E-band and non-terrestrial network (NTN) of connecting things before and after, so it is foreseeable that mobile communications will always maintain a strong vitality.

2.1.2 *Application scenarios*

According to the forecast of IMT 2020 (5G) promotion group, the global mobile Internet data traffic in 2030 will increase by 50 times that in 2020, reaching the terminal scale of 100 billion. 5G will push the whole society into a new era of "intelligent connection of all things" and "people-centered" between people (natural and legal persons) and people, people and things, and things and things.

The ITU defines the three application scenarios: eMBB, ultra-reliable low-latency communications (uRLLC), and massive machine type communications (mMTC). Going forward, it has locked in the requirements of diverse kinds of applications, such as AR (augmented reality)/VR (virtual reality), autonomous driving, unmanned aerial vehicle, smart power grid, and telemedicine. According to the objects, it is classified into main categories of to-consumer (2C), to-home (2H), to-business (2B), and other multi-level markets. As shown in Table 2.1, 5G technology needs to have different basic capabilities in different scenarios and applications.

In the 5G era, technology no longer just changes or upgrades a particular user experience, but instead develops killer scenarios, providing solutions for specialized scenarios in many different aspects of personal life, family, business, and industry. As shown in Table 2.2, 5G technology is expected to create great social value. It is true that "4G changes individuals and 5G reshapes society".

Table 2.1 Basic capabilities of 5G technology.

Competency index	Competency definition	Application scenario	Minimum requirement of data transfer rate
Peak rate	Maximum rate that a single user or device can obtain under ideal conditions (unit: Gb/s)	eMBB, uRLLC, mMTC	Downlink data transmission rate is 20 Gb/s The uplink data transmission rate is 10 Gb/s
User experience rate	The minimum guaranteed rate that mobile users or terminals can obtain anywhere in the coverage area (unit: Mb/s or Gb/s)	eMBB	The downlink data transmission rate is 100 Mb/s The uplink data transmission rate is 50Mb/S
Mobility	The maximum moving speed (unit: km/h) when wireless devices in Multi-layer/Multi-RAT meet specific QoS (quality of service) and transmit without packet loss or call drop	eMBB	500 km/h
Time delay	User plane delay: the time consumed by the wireless network in the process of sending data packets from the source to the destination (unit: ms); Control plane delay: the transition time from IDLE state (standby state) to ACTIVE state (active state) of the terminal (unit: ms)	eMBB, uRLLC	Control plane: 10 ms User plane: 4 ms/1 ms for eMBB/uRLLC
Regional flow	Total throughput per geographical area [unit: Mb/(s·m^2)]	eMBB	10 Mb/(s·m^2)
Connection density	Total number of connected or accessed devices per unit area (unit: devices/km^2)	eMTC (enhanced machine type communication)	1 000 000 devices/km^2
Connection density	The number of bits that can be received/transmitted from the network per joule of energy (unit: b/J)	eMBB, eMTC	5G is 100 times higher than 4G
Spectral efficiency	Average throughput per cell or unit area provided by unit spectrum resources [unit: b/(s·Hz)]	eMBB, uRLLC, eMTC	5G is 3 times higher than 4G

Table 2.2 5G reshapes society.

5G applications	5G basic capability requirements	Professional competence	Application case and value
AR/VR	Rate: 100 Mb/s–9.4 Gb/s; Time delay: 2–10 ms	Cloud rendering; convergence of communication, computing and storage	360° live broadcast of apparel marketing, teaching interaction, tourism promotion, new media and other fields; new economic value
Smart creation	Rate: 10 Mb/s; Time delay: 1 ms	99.999% reliability (defined as the probability of successful data transmission); robots; industry communication, computing and storage networks	Factory automation; industry 4.0
Smart driving	Remote driving field: speed: uplink 25 Mb/s, downlink 1 Mb/s; Time delay: 5 ms	99.999% reliability; fusion perception: Camera/LiDAR/millimeter-wave radar; virtual to virtual (V2V)/device to device (D2D); artificial intelligence	Formation and automatic driving; save lives; save energy; reduce pollution

2.2 5G Spectrum: The Raw Materials in the Hands of Craftsmen

Spectrum, operating license, and site resources have always been the core resources of mobile operators. The identification, use, and network construction of the 5G spectrum are particularly important, reflecting the wisdom of top-level competition between countries.

2.2.1 *5G spectrum identification*

As shown in Tables 2.3 and 2.4, 5G New Radio (NR) defined the divided spectrum resources into two different frequency ranges (FRs), namely

Table 2.3 5G FR1 spectrum resource allocation.

NR band number	Uplink frequency band Base station reception/ UE transmission	Downlink frequency band Base station transmission/ UE reception	Duplex mode
n1	1920–1980 MHz	2110–2170 MHz	FDD
n2	1850–1910 MHz	1930–1990 MHz	FDD
n3	1710–1785 MHz	1805–1880 MHz	FDD
n5	824–849 MHz	869–894 MHz	FDD
n7	2500–2570 MHz	2620–2690 MHz	FDD
n8	880–915 MHz	925–960 MHz	FDD
n20	832–862 MHz	791–821 MHz	FDD
n28	703–748 MHz	758–803 MHz	FDD
n38	2570–2620 MHz	2570–2620 MHz	TDD
n41	2496–2690 MHz	2496–2690 MHz	TDD
n50	1432–1517 MHz	1432–1517 MHz	TDD
n51	1427–1432 MHz	1427–1432 MHz	TDD
n66	1710–1780 MHz	2110–2200 MHz	FDD
n70	1695–1710 MHz	1995–2020 MHz	FDD
n71	663–698 MHz	617–652 MHz	FDD
n74	1427–1470 MHz	1475–1518 MHz	FDD
n75	N/A	1432–1517 MHz	SDL
n76	N/A	1427–1432 MHz	SDL
n77	3300–4200 MHz	3300–4200 MHz	TDD
n78	3300–3800 MHz	3300–3800 MHz	TDD
n79	4400–5000 MHz	4400–5000 MHz	TDD
n80	1710–1785 MHz	N/A	SUL
n81	880–915 MHz	N/A	SUL
n82	832–862 MHz	N/A	SUL
n83	703–748 MHz	N/A	SUL
n84	1920–1980 MHz	N/A	SUL

FR1 and FR2. FR1 is a sub-6 GHz frequency band (under 6 GHz, 450–6000 MHz frequency range), with 11 kinds of carrier bandwidths, such as 5/10/15/20/25/30/40/50/60/80/100 MHz. FR2 is a 5G millimeter-wave frequency band (24.25–52.6 GHz frequency range), with four kinds

Table 2.4 5G FR2 spectrum resource allocation.

NR band number	Uplink/downlink frequency band Base station reception/UE transmission	Duplex mode
n257	26,500–29,500 MHz	TDD
n258	24,250–27,500 MHz	TDD
n260	37,000–40,000 MHz	TDD

of carrier bandwidths, such as 50/100/200/400 MHz. 5G introduces the supplementary uplink (SUL) and supplementary downlink (SDL) bands based on the 4G TDD and FDD duplex. Working with millimeter wave 2.8 GHz or 3.5 GHz/4.9 GHz of C-band, the SUL band can make up for the defect of weak uplink coverage ability on the base station. SUL can also compensate for the shortcoming of uplink capacity insufficiency in the TDD ratio spectrum arising from the time slot matching (e.g., 8:2 for downlink and uplink time slot matching), resulting in better safeguard of businesses such as video monitoring which is dominated by uplink transportation. At present, China Telecom has selected 1.8 GHz and 2.1 GHz bands as the matching SUL of C-band. SDL can greatly improve the downlink, unicast, multicast, and broadcast capabilities of base stations with high commercial value to be explored in the future.

Unlike LTE bands, which begin with a "Band", 5G bands begin with an "n". The spectrum that evolved from LTE to NR is called refarming, and for this, software radio technology is used to share spectrum resources in the physical layer of both LTE and NR users in a set of base station equipment or to upgrade LTE to NR on demand.

China and Europe have always attached great importance to the unified global spectrum, industry chain, and standardization, so they unanimously preferred FR1 for the commercial use of 5G. The United States, out of confidence in its own millimeter-wave industry and the desire to lead the industry, preferred FR2. Among the above spectrum, n77, n78, and n79, i.e., 3.3–4.2 GHz, 3.3–3.8 GHz, and 4.4–5.0 GHz or n257, n258, and n260, i.e., MMW frequency band 26 GHz/28 GHz/39 GHz are the new spectrums and form the selection for the first wave of 5G construction for most carriers. According to their national conditions and operation strategies, different countries will carry out the second wave of 5G construction in the new frequency band represented by n28 (700 MHz) and the reframed medium frequency band represented by n1 (1800 MHz).

2.2.2 The use of 5G spectrum

5G spectrum is classified into two kinds: authorized spectrum and unauthorized spectrum. At present, the authorized spectrum of public mobile communications (as shown in Tables 2.3 and 2.4) possessed by the carrier is used commercially.

With vigorous promotion in countries across the world, the private network licensing spectrum developed quickly. In Germany, manufacturers such as Volkswagen, Siemens, Bosch, BASF, and ABB have proposed to build their own 5G private network. Therefore, Germany has defined the 3.7–3.8 GHz (100 MHz bandwidth in total) as the authorized spectrum of the 5G private network. The Ministry of Communications of Japan plans to complete the 5G private network spectrum institutionalization and specification of a complete set of assignments in 2020. This program, called the Local 5G, aims to achieve 5G innovative applications across the industry by opening 5G private network spectrum and assisting the vertical industry (including research facilities, airports, factories, parks, and gymnasiums) of non-telecom carriers, thus creating a higher economic value. China has also clarified that the 5.9 GHz band should be applied to 5G V2X (Vehicle to Everything). In the unauthorized frequency spectrum, 3GPP has considered the 60 GHz unauthorized frequency spectrum for the new version of 5G standard R17 (R17 expands the frequency band range of 5G NR from 52.6 GHz to 71 GHz), and then the unlicensed NR will be formed in the end.

The 5G spectrum distribution in China is shown in Table 2.5. It is characterized by the participation of a new operator, China Radio & Television Network Co., Ltd., which promotes a diversified competition pattern. The State Grid may also use the 700 MHz spectrum of China Radio & Television to build a national smart grid. Each frequency band

Table 2.5 Distribution of 5G spectrum in China.

Operator	5G Spectrum
China Mobile	n41: 2515–2675 MHz, total 160 MHz; n79: 4800–4900 MHz, total 100 MHz
China Telecom	n78: 3400–3500 MHz, total 100 MHz
China Unicom	n78: 3500–3600 MHz, total 100 MHz
China Radio and Television	n79: 4900–5000 MHz, total 100 MHz; n28: 703–748 MHz/758–803 MHz, total 2 × 45 MHz

has a large bandwidth of more than 100 MHz. With the broadband of radio frequency channels and optical transmission resources, transmission cost and bit energy consumption can be reduced several times, reflecting the advantages of equipment acquisition and network operation compared with 4G. Considering that sub-6 GHz is more mature than MMW in the global industry, sub-6 GHz is mainly promoted.

2.2.3 *5G network construction*

As mentioned above, 5G standardization and spectrum formulation developed at a fast pace, then what will the future of the 5G network look like? In the construction of the 5G network, the requirements of capacity, coverage, equipment utilization rate, and function expansion should be considered first. The FR1 band can ensure the basic customer experience of 5G due to its characteristics of low frequency and strong coverage ability, making it suitable to be used as an underlying network. Sub-6 GHz has a large number of 2G, 3G, and 4G applications, which need to be gradually upgraded from 2G and 3G to 5G after various conditions (especially terminal) are ready. FR2, the millimeter-wave frequency band, has a weak penetration ability, but it has sufficient bandwidth and less interference, which can ensure customers' extreme experience. What is more, millimeter wave, with the characteristics of small size and easy deployment, can realize functions, such as positioning and perception. So, it has great application potential in outdoor hot spots, industrial scenes, and indoor digitization.

Due to the diversity and the openness of the standards of the 5G spectrum, companies and industries can set up their exclusive 5G systems just like IT construction. 5G can become a company's core competitive element and react with other corporate elements to form new production capacity. Enterprises can build their own 5G networks using license-free and special-purpose spectrum, rent 5G networks from carriers, and delegate their own special-purpose spectrum to carriers.

China's 5G network construction shows a highly prosperous trend. China Telecom and China Unicom discussed the low-cost sharing construction mode at 2.1 GHz and 3.5 GHz. China Telecom is actively exploring the complementary SUL mode combining 3.5 GHz and medium band (1.8/2.1 GHz). China Radio & Television Network actively explored the use of 700 MHz to expand 5G network construction into new media, three-network integration, and vertical industry.

Taking advantage of 2.6 GHz with both coverage and capacity, China Mobile first adopted active massive MIMO (MM) equipment configuration. In addition, relevant Chinese institutions and departments are also actively experimenting with the millimeter-wave frequency band and releasing the frequency band at the right time to store up energy for the sustainable development of 5G.

At present, China is in the first tier around the world regarding aspects of 5G standards, equipment manufacturing, industry, and terminal carriers. This situation is expected to push forward the progress of basic industries, such as material, equipment manufacturing, microelectronics, and application industries, such as computing, storage, and sensing. Meanwhile, through coordinated development with scientific and technological innovations, 5G is becoming one of the most important engines of China's economic development. In the "New Infrastructure Construction" plan launched by the central government in 2020, 5G occupied a core position.

2.3 5G System Introduction: The First Acquaintance of Lushan's True Face

2.3.1 *The overall situation*

5G system is a very complex end-to-end communication system. In order to explain the complex 5G system to you in simple words, we must first introduce a few basic principles of the 5G system:

1. *Design principles of RAN, core network, and terminal*: Network Elements (NEs) are the basic units of a set of output information, which is generated by some input information. This input and output information is used to communicate with other NEs. For example, the base station NE uses radio wave signals as input and outputs voice and other bit information to the core network through functions such as radio frequency processing and baseband signal demodulation. The core network NE generates customer-perceived multimedia (such as AR/VR) and completes the routing function. The mobile communication system should ensure that the function of the network element is clear, the interface between the network elements is clear, and the network elements can interoperate, which are usually accomplished through a series of functions, interfaces, protocols, and tests.

2. Based on the service-based architecture (SBA) principle, the secret of the mobile communication development is service-driven design, which means standards' establishment and network construction, while application development as well as alliance building should be based on a certain service-driven vision (e.g., 5G eMBB, uRLLC, and mMTC) to boost consumer experience (2C) and empowered industry (2B) trial services, implementing network optimization and flexible expansion according to the closed-loop service. In the early stage, the 3GPP supports circuit switching architecture driven by fixed services (such as voice and short message). Starting with Release 5 (the Fifth Release) of 3GPP, the open IP data interchange architecture became the mainstream of the 5G network. 5G's business is more complex than that of the previous four generations, requiring a high degree of flexibility while opening up multiple services. In order to meet this requirement, 5G slicing security technology came into being. 5G slicing is a mechanism for different services to share network resources. The service proportion of macro stations and hot spots of public network, enterprise network, and home network is different according to the different deployment environments. Even for the same base station, the service composition may also change greatly over time. For instance, in the early stage, the network is oriented toward eMBB, but in the later stage, the proportion of eMTC and wireless broadband integrated into the home is greatly increased, so the 5G network must be elastic to be quickly deployed at low cost. This elasticity can be achieved through network element decoupling, programmability, reconfigurable computing, and other methods. This requirement is ensured through 5G Software-Defined Network (SDN)/Network Function Virtualization (NFV). Moreover, 5G must also respond quickly to business requirements and save bandwidth with low latency. To realize this function, we need to introduce the Content Delivery Network (CDN) system similar to wired Internet video. The 5G core network is divided into centralized 5G core and sunken Mobile Edge Computing (MEC).
3. *Principle of Efficiency (Spectrum Efficiency/Power Efficiency/Site Efficiency) Priority*: Wireless open port (Uu) technology of mobile communication aims to provide maximum throughput [B/(S · Hz)], i.e., spectrum efficiency, with the same spectrum. Constrained by Shannon's law, the higher the signal-to-noise ratio, the greater the minimum number of transceiver antennas, and the more the users of

the same frequency simultaneously, the higher the spectral efficiency. 4G mainly relies on MIMO+OFDMA, while 5G mainly relies on flexible service scheduling and massive MIMO to improve spectrum efficiency.

The introduction of more antennas to 5G terminals [from 1T2R (1 send and 2 receive) to 2T4R (2 send and 4 receive)] and the introduction of more antennas to networks (from 2T2R to 32T32R and above) may lead to increased power consumption of devices. In order to solve this problem, on the one hand, it relies on power linearization technology and semiconductor technology optimization. On the other hand, if 5G throughput is significantly improved compared with 4G throughput, unit bit energy consumption will also decrease by orders of magnitude. For instance, when the base station is developed from the traditional 4T4R to massive MIMO, the capacity will increase by 3–5 times generally if the power consumption is doubled. 5G power efficiency will be greatly improved just in the sense of bits.

Whether from the perspective of antenna combining remote radio unit (RRU) or the angle of active antenna, carriers must place multiple frequency bands equipment (base station) in the limited site space and provide as much as possible signal processing of ports in order to improve the capacity, which is the so-called site efficiency and is bound to be rigidly constrained by Maxwell's law. Multi-band multiport antenna, high-efficiency filter, high-efficiency power amplifier, multi-band antenna, and RF integration technology have become the key to improving the efficiency of the 5G site.

4. *Terminal diversity principle*: Besides regular smartphones, 5G terminals will carry more of the "end-everything" of the whole scene, which will take on various and strange forms. Due to the difference of home, enterprise, and industry scenarios and dynamic changes in requirements, terminal openness, security and the ability to fuse computing, storage, and perception, location and AI have become the key to the success or failure of the 5G network.

2.3.2 *Wireless access*

Like other intergenerational evolution versions in mobile communication, wireless air interface and wireless network architecture have become the most important features of 5G. In the long run, 5G will coexist with LTE, NB-IoT, and their long-term evolution versions that support low bandwidth (1.4–20 MHz). Therefore, 5G's inheritance of the main features of LTE air interface layering (PHY/MAC/RLC/PDCP/RRC/etc.) and frame structure are beneficial to network deployment, flexible spectrum usage, and reducing system complexity.

2.3.2.1 *Wireless air interface*

The following factors are the main consideration for the 5G air interface:

(1) *Business diversity*: 4G focuses on communication between people, which is the mobile Internet, while 5G needs to ensure everything is connected in addition to further enhancing the mobile Internet. Business in the 5G era will be unprecedentedly prosperous, no matter the millisecond delay required for remote real-time control, or the Gb/s bandwidth required for AR/VR and ultra-HD video, or the wide coverage and low power consumption of Internet of Everything with millions of connections per square kilometer with greatly different requirements in the design of the air interface.
(2) *Business extension*: 5G will extend the boundaries of mobile communications, embrace different industries and become an efficiency booster. But compared with the mobile Internet business, the requirements of vertical industries vary greatly. The so-called "long tail" feature where there are different business needs and small total business value in each business determines that it is impossible to customize an air interface for each industry requirement. So, different parameter configurations should be used to adapt to different industry requirements with long tail under the unified air interface framework.
(3) *Business uncertainty*: The future is always beyond our imagination. We have to admit that there are too many uncertainties in the next 4–5 years, and new unpredictable businesses may be formed and developed rapidly with some technological innovations. In the face of 5G future development, it is necessary to consider both the driving force of business and the appropriate advancement of technology so as to cope with the uncertainty of future business and realize the dual driver of business and technology.

To sum up, 5G NR, also known as 5G new radio technology, defines the protocol part between mobile terminals and base stations. In order to handle the diversity, extension, and uncertainty of 5G services in

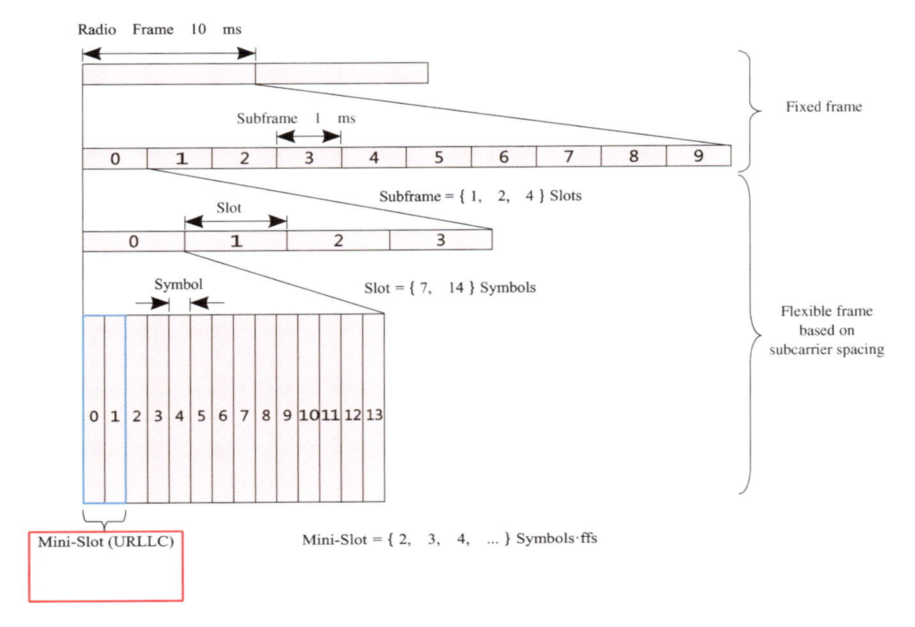

Figure 2.2 5G NR flexible frame structure.

the future, the main strategies of 5G air interface design will include uniformity, flexibility, and standards compatibility, which are extensively embodied in the frame structure design (Fig. 2.2).

The frame structure of 5G is based on Orthogonal Frequency Division Multiple Access (OFDMA). Uniformity refers to the ability of FR1 and FR2 to support different bandwidths, different services, and FDD/TDD/SUL/SDL. Flexibility refers to supporting the matching and combination of different businesses based on the business conditions. Standard compatibility refers to maintaining a frame structure similar to LTE as well as supporting subsequent airport upgrades and business definitions.

2.3.2.2 *The wireless network*

From 3G to 4G and even 5G, some aspects are relatively unchanged, as shown in Figs. 2.3 and 2.4. First, the network is divided into two parts: RAN and CN. RAN in 3G, 4G, and 5G involves RNC and Node B (3G mobile base station), evolved Node B station (eNB) and next-generation NodeB station (gNB), respectively. RAN has been aimed at improving

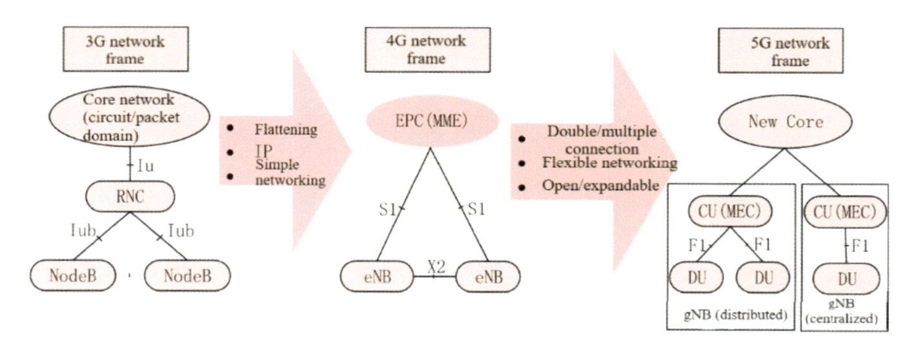

Figure 2.3 Changes of wireless access networks from 3G to 5G.

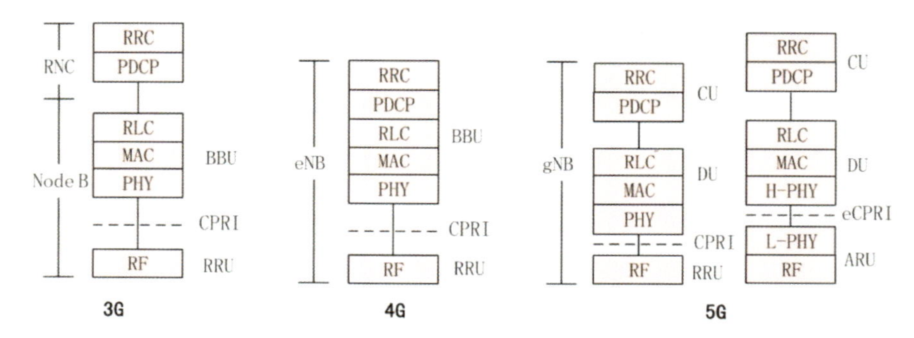

Figure 2.4 5G protocol and equipment mapping.

spectrum efficiency and power efficiency, divided into baseband and RF transformation (RF), physical layer (PHY), codecs, modem, etc., multi-user resource scheduling and retransmission of error correction (MAC), wireless link control (RLC), such as reliable and orderly data transmission, packet data gathering protocol (PDCP), such as protocol header compression and decryption encryption and wireless resource control (RRC), such as power control, switch control and congestion control protocol hierarchy. From 3G to 4G and even 5G, the changes seen are the redefinition and combination of network elements as well as the evolution and revolution of each protocol layer, but there is no structural change in the key protocol layer.

A mobile communication fronthaul (as shown in Fig. 2.4) refers to the BBU pool connecting to a remote RRU portion, whose capacity of the link depends primarily on the wireless air interface rate and the number of

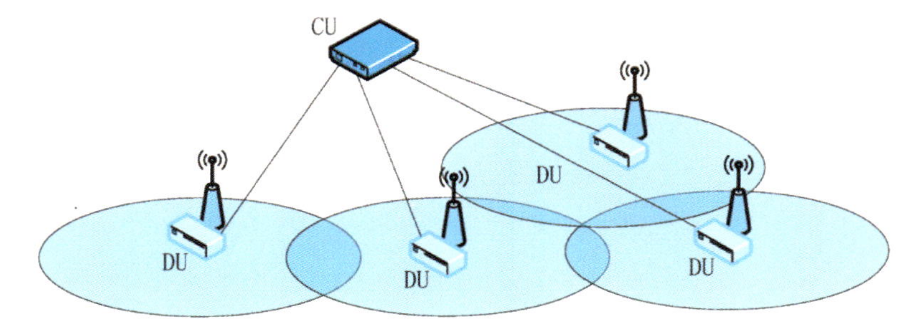

Figure 2.5 Distributed deployment of CU centralized DU.

MIMO antennas. The 4G fronthaul link adopts Common Public Radio Interface (CPRI) protocol. In the 5G phase, its spectrum bandwidth causes a soaring wireless rate, MIMO antenna number to increase multiple times, and CPRI is unable to meet the 5G capacity and fronthaul requirements. Therefore, standards organizations are actively researching new fronthaul technology, including taking some processing capacity from BBU to RRU unit (L-PHY in the figure), to reduce the time delay and fronthaul capacity, thus forming enhanced CPRI (eCPRI).

Compared with 4G, 5G has the following changes:

(1) *High-level division*: gNB is divided into center unit (CU) and distribution unit (DU), as shown in Figs. 2.4 and 2.5. CU and DU can be combined to form a centralized base station, which is mainly used for macro base stations with wide coverage. CU and DU can constitute a distributed base station system, which is mainly suitable for the intensive networking and the coordinated processing of macro stations and their micro base stations. DU is mainly close to the base station antenna. CU is mainly close to the service convergence point.
(2) *Bottom level division*: Considering the increase of 5G antenna ports and RF bandwidth, part of the physical layer processing function (L-PHY) is close to RF to realize optimal active antenna. The unit that only includes RF is called RRU. The unit that includes L-PHY is called ARU, which is an active radio unit or an active antenna.
(3) *Core network differentiation*: There are mainly MEC and New Core. MEC considers more about the network edge close to the user side. For example, it can share a common server physical entity with CU to achieve logical separation.

(4) *Centralized deployment for CU and distributed deployment for DU*: As shown in Fig. 2.5, this deployment architecture is well suited to hot spots. If the CU and DU in the figure are replaced with BBU and RRU, respectively, a traditional cloud radio access network (C-RAN) can be formed. C-RAN is more conducive to physical layer collaboration and efficient resource scheduling, achieving higher spectral efficiency.

2.3.3 *System architecture*

The network of carriers includes a large number of network element equipment, which directly leads to problems such as high cost of upgrading equipment, slow launch time, and difficult network optimization. So, choosing the right system architecture is particularly important.

2.3.3.1 *SDN/NFV: 5G methodology*

As an emerging network architecture, SDN decouples the control plane and data plane, while it also centralizes the functions, making the control panel software programmable. In traditional networks, the distributed control plane works at various network nodes (such as base station controllers, switches, and routers), so all network equipment must be upgraded if a new network function is to be deployed, which greatly limits the evolution and upgrade of the network. SDN adopts a centralized control plane and a distributed data plane which are separated from each other. So, the control plane centrally controls the devices on the data plane with a communication interface, providing flexible programmability to fully solve the problems between the coupling of the control plane and the data plane.

NFV is a technology that integrates network functions into industry-standard servers, provides an optimized virtualized data plane and could replace traditional physical network equipment with the software running on the server. With NFV, the middleware deployed in the existing network could be reduced or even removed, and a single physical platform could be run on different applications. NFV is suitable for any data plane and control plane functions, for either fixed or mobile networks, as well as for the automation of management and configuration requiring scalability.

In conclusion, the role of SDN and NFV in 5G can be summarized as follows: SDN technology is a solution to the coupling problem between network control plane and data plane, and the adoption of SDN technology makes the deployment of user plane functions more flexible. Deploying user flat features closer to the user's wireless access network can improve the user experience, e.g., reducing latency. The NFV technology was proposed as a solution to the problem of the highly coupled software and hardware of evolved packet core (EPC). It enabled carriers to deploy network capabilities in common servers, switches, and storage devices, greatly reducing time and cost.

In the 5G mobile communication system, SDN and NFV technologies will play an important role in enabling network power, realizing flexibility, ductility, and service-oriented management. Flexibility is the realization of on-demand availability and customization of functionality. Ductility refers to the ability to meet conflicting business requirements, such as supporting enhanced mobile broadband (eMBB) services, mMTC services, and ultra-high-reliability and ultra-low latency (uRLLC) services by introducing appropriate access processes and modes of transmission. Service-oriented management will be achieved through a thread-based control plane and a user plane of joint framework based on NFV and SDN.

Figure 2.6 shows the 5G network architecture based on SDN/NFV. A brief introduction of 5G network elements is shown in Table 2.6.

2.3.3.2 *NSA and SA: Evolution of enabling network*

The 5G NR standard provides two networking schemes (Fig. 2.7) which are Non-standalone (NSA) and Standalone (SA), respectively.

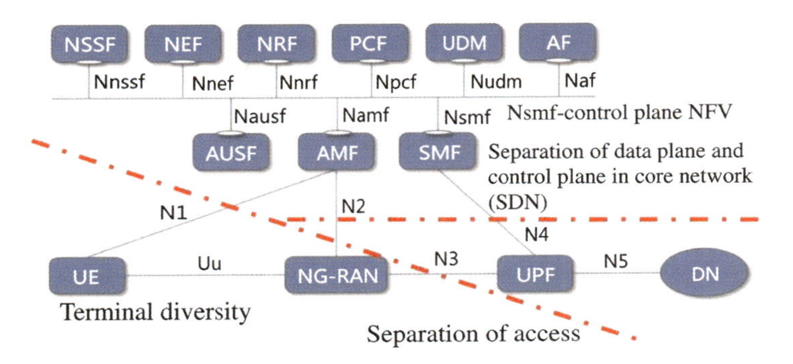

Figure 2.6 Overall frame of 5G network.

Table 2.6 Brief introduction of core network elements.

5G network elements	Brief introduction
AUSF: authentication server function	UE authentication and certification
AMF: access and mobility management function	Registration, connection and mobility management
AF: application function	Application functions
DN: data network	Data network
PCF: policy control function	Obtain contract from UDM and issue to AMF, etc.
NEF: network exposure function	Network exposure function
NRF: network repository function	Network repository function
NSSF: network slice selection function	Slice instances that serve the UE
SMF: session management function	Session management (including IP assignment)
UDM: unified data management	Contract data management
UPF: user plane function	User plane routing and packet forwarding

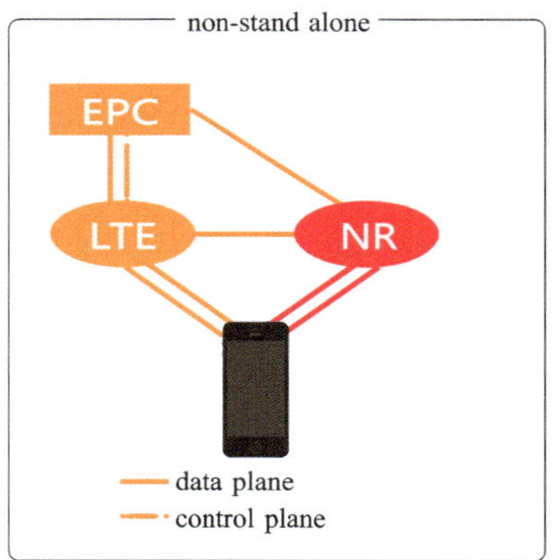

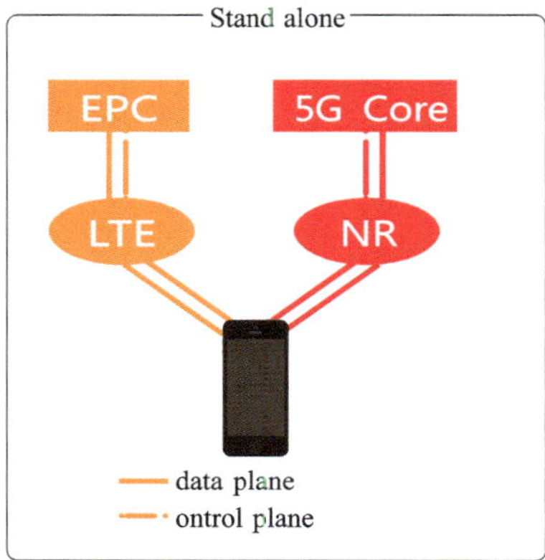

Figure 2.7 NSA and SA network deployment.

As a transition program, NSA mainly aims to improve the bandwidth of hot spot areas and operate by making use of the original 4G base station and 4G core network to upgrade. The 5G carriers based on the NSA architecture carry only user data and their control signaling is still transmitted over 4G networks. Their deployment can be regarded as an expansion of existing 4G networks by adding new carriers. The carrier can determine the upgrade site and area according to the business requirements, which does not necessarily require complete contiguous coverage. In a world where 5G coverage is not yet complete, the NSA architecture helps ensure a good user experience. The NSA is not good at supporting businesses of Internet of things (IoT) and network slices of the 5G network.

SA can realize all the new features of 5G, which is conducive to giving full play to all functions of 5G, recognized as the 5G target plan in the industry. SA has the advantages of both 4G and 5G, such as being able to choose different manufacturers, having strong business capability, and avoiding the transformation of the 4G access network by NSA. Therefore, the three major operators in China use SA as the preferred network construction plan. SA needs to invest in the construction of the 5G core network and continuous coverage access network at the initial stage of network construction, which is also a factor that operators have to consider due to the high initial cost.

2.3.3.3 *Network slicing: Scenes of rich enabling*

5G network section refers to mutual isolation, automation, and quickly launched virtual network built on a unified 5G network, which can meet the requirements of particular businesses (uplink high rate on the video monitoring, low latency, and high reliability on power grid monitoring) and provide differentiated service guarantee on the basis of the service level agreement (SLA).

Tenants order network slices from carriers online through their own portal or Application Programming Interface (API) gateway and submit relevant requirements to Communication Service Management Function (CSMF), such as the online number of users, average rate, delay, security isolation, business type, cost, and coverage area. The SLA requirements that the CSMF converts into a network slice are composed and assigned to each level of network element for execution. CSMF can provide tenants with a visual representation of the state of the network slice.

As shown in Fig. 2.8, according to different service requirements, the physical network can be sliced into multiple virtual networks, including smartphone (eMBB), automatic driving (V2X), and large-scale Internet of Things (eMTC) slicing network.

Network slice features end-to-end network security SLA, business isolation, on-demand customization of network functions, and automation.

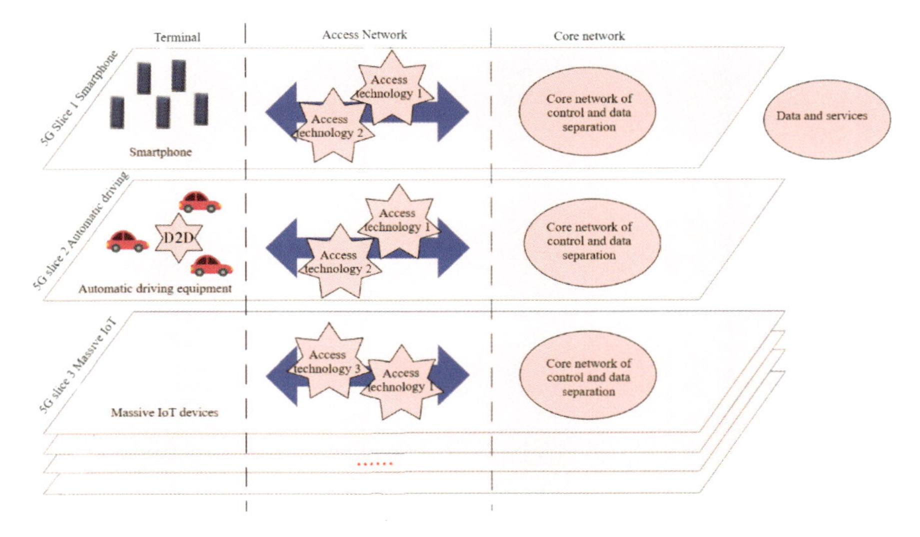

Figure 2.8 Network slicing diagram.

(1) Network slicing achieves multi-domain collaboration and SLA decomposition when a network slicing device is connected to wireless Internet and transmitted to multiple network domains such as the core network and even terminals.
(2) Different slices share hardware resources and transmittable resources, but different business instances are constructed, which are logically isolated from each other to ensure their network security, reliability, and non-interference by themselves.
(3) Network slices are customized as required and dynamically composed. However, it is necessary to provide the tenant operation and maintenance personnel with a working interface that is easy to observe, operate, and control.
(4) Automatic network operation and maintenance are carried out. From the perspective of carriers, network slice has introduced a new business operation mode, which can better serve customers, especially those in vertical industries, to achieve the best economic benefits. From the perspective of tenants, on the basis of operation and maintenance participation, huge costs and risks of constructing a private network can be avoided to focus on core value creation. From the perspective of the 3GPP protocol, network slicing depends to a large extent on the specific implementation of each vendor, so there is no

detailed standardization on relevant resource management. As a result, the best solution should be found in practice for network slicing.

2.3.3.4 *Edge computing: Multiple applications of enabling*

MEC originally stood for mobile edge computing, which was defined as "IT and cloud computing capabilities provided by wireless access networks near mobile users", emphasizing the proximity and availability of services. So far, MEC's functions are no longer limited to literal mobile networks when multi-access MEC becomes available, which also covers non-3GPP access (such as Wi-Fi and fixed networks) and is a universal service multiplier. MEC is broadly defined as "providing cloud computing capabilities and AN IT services environment on the edge of the network for application developers and content providers".

To demonstrate the value of MEC, some typical application scenarios are provided as follows:

Scenario 1: In the scenario of intelligent security, the combination of edge computing and video surveillance technology can improve the intelligent processing capability of the front-end camera of the video surveillance system in view of public security problems such as new crimes and social governance.

Scenario 2: Distributed caching can save backhaul and transmission data traffic, reduce latency, improve quality of experience (QoE), and reduce video lag.

Scenario 3: Hundreds of sensors in a self-driving car will generate terabytes of data per hour. From a security perspective, the combination of MEC and cloud computing will enable the car to avoid sudden hazards in an emergency.

Scenario 4: In the case of backtrip communication failure, the local edge computing node can still provide communication and application support for the local devices connected to the node to complete the off-grid information service.

To sum up, 5G MEC can greatly improve the system's speed, reduce delay, and improve performance such as security. Terminals will face bandwidth limitations caused by network capabilities and terminal complexity. As the number of connections between network access nodes keeps increasing, a massive amount of data will be generated. If all data have to be returned to the cloud for analysis and termination, it will not only waste bandwidth but also increase the delay.

A large amount of data need to be analyzed, processed, and stored while these data conform to the application paradigm of artificial intelligence, which is "data + model + algorithm = AI". A large amount of data has the characteristics of regionalization and specialization, especially for industry and enterprise data. The massive increase of 5G terminals will create a lot of security problems (such as agent attacks and network disconnection), which can be solved by MEC's function of security isolation. MEC deployment has the characteristics of general computing platform customization and software programmable reconstruction, which will play a greater role in the 5G era. In a sense, without MEC, 5G business goals might not have been achieved.

MEC and cloud computing are in the relationship of complementarity. Cloud computing holds the whole, focusing on non-real-time, long-cycle, and cross-regional data analysis, which makes better use of its strengths in the fields of periodic maintenance and data mining. MEC, on the other hand, focuses on local, real-time, and short-cycle data analysis, which can better support real-time intelligent processing and execution of local business. Therefore, from the perspective of the business side, the two technologies complement each other naturally and jointly constitute 5G Network as a Service (5GaaS).

MEC provides an opportunity for carriers, enterprises, and industries to adopt a new model, thus reducing costs and improving competitiveness at the same time. MEC dedicated either to the public network or private network can become the core asset of enterprises and industries. The following strategies need to be considered during the actual deployment of the carriers:

(1) Transform the wireless access node into an intelligent service center that can directly provide highly personalized services from the edge of the network while providing the best performance in the communication network.
(2) It can be fused and deployed on different servers. 5G applications are most likely to fuse with DU functions.

From the device level, MEC supports heterogeneous hardware combinations, such as Graphics Processing Unit (GPU), Network processor (NP), and AI. It should have customizable performance, integration, and power consumption capabilities. Meanwhile, MEC supports one-stop integration and plug-and-play for users to achieve rapid business delivery easily.

2.3.4 *Terminals*

In the face of requirements from business capacity, cost, coverage, and power consumption, how to choose the right terminal is one of the most important considerations in building 5G solutions. More than 150 new 5G mobile phones and customer premise equipment (CPE) will be launched in 2019, with an industrial-grade module expected by the end of 2020. Although 5G terminal category has not yet formed relevant standards, the LTE terminal category (Cat) principle still has important reference significance. Table 2.7 provides the terminal classification of LTE from Cat 0 to Cat 12, and the related explanations are as follows:

(1) Terminal capacity reflects the transmission rates of uplink and downlink peaks. The actual users' perception rate is related to their environment, the state of the base station, and the number of users.

Table 2.7 LTE terminal types.

Grade	Downlink peak transmission rate (Mb/s)	Number of MIMO streams	Uplink peak transmission rate (Mb/s)	Standard
Cat 0	0.2	1	0.2	R12
Cat 1	10	1	5	R8
Cat 2	50	2	25	R8
Cat 3	100	2	50	R8
Cat 4	150	2	50	R8
Cat 5	300	4	75	R8
Cat 6	300	2/4	50	R10
Cat 7	300	2/4	150	R10
Cat 8	1200	8	600	R10
Cat 9	450	2/4	50	R11
Cat 10	450	2/4	100	R11
Cat 11	600	2/4	50	R12
Cat 12	450	2/4	100	R12

(2) The transmission rate of terminal peak is the result of a combination of the number of end-user antennas (typically 2 antennas, partly 4/8 antennas), rf complexity, modulation capability, and spectrum bandwidth. A MIMO stream number of 4 means that the terminal has at least 4 antennas. The uplink capability of Cat 7/Cat 8 is improved due to uplink support for more advanced modulation (from 16QAM to 64QAM, up to 4 B/Hz to 6 B/Hz). The Cat 8 capability is enhanced by the use of basic bandwidth aggregation (20–40 MHz or higher).
(3) Not all terminal levels will be accepted by the market. Most carriers choose Cat 4 and Cat 6 instead of Cat 5 because Cat 4 only requires an RRU of 2 send and 2 receive, while Cat 5 requires an RRU of 4 send and 4 receive. In addition, Cat 5 requires terminal support for high-order modulation, which results in an extremely high terminal cost and power efficiency, while Cat 6 has relatively loose requirements for base stations and terminal sides.
(4) Different terminals have different functionalities. Cat 8 is aimed at WTTc (Wireless to consumer) or WTTe (Wireless to Enterprise). Cat 0 (NB-IoT), Cat 1 (eMTC), and Cat 4 target the low- to mid-end IoT, respectively. Cat 4 can be used for high-speed data, such as live broadcasts and Internet of vehicles. Cat 1 can be used for shared bikes and mobile POS terminals and Cat 0 can be used for electricity meters.

Let's focus on Cat 0 or Nb-IoT. Cat 0 aims to support wide-area NB-IoT applications including wearables, smart homes, and smart meters through low-power, low-cost, and wide-range devices. In order to reduce the cost and even power consumption by lowering the complexity, the technical measures adopted include supporting FDD half-duplex mode, reducing bandwidth to 1.4 MHz, single dispatch, single-receipt link, reducing requirements of communication, computing, and storage resource, and adopting low data rate mode. The terminal cost of Cat 0 is expected to be at least 75% lower than that of Cat 4.

To reduce power consumption and increase the service life of the battery, Cat 0 supports the power-saving mode (PSM) plan. If the device supports PSM, during the process of attachment or tracking area update (TAU), PSM is applied to the network for the values of an activation timer. When the equipment moves from the connection state to the idle state, the timer starts to run. When the timer stops, the device enters power-saving mode and no longer receives paging messages until the device needs to actively send messages to the network. With the PSM, two no. 5 batteries can be used for several years. In order to increase the coverage, in addition to selecting the sub-1 GHz frequency band for the base station side, working under the condition of low SNR can also be considered.

A key feature of 5G terminals is the introduction of bandwidth part (BWP) technology. BWP is a combination of continuous physical resource blocks (PRBs) within a given carrier. The introduction of the BWP is primarily intended to enable user equipment (UE) to make better use of the larger carrier bandwidth (e.g., 100 MHz in the C-band and 400 MHz in the MM band). For a large carrier bandwidth, if UE is used to detect and maintain the full bandwidth in real time, it will bring about great challenges to the terminal energy consumption.

The introduction of the BWP concept is to carve out a portion of the bandwidth from the entire large carrier to the UE for access and data transmission. UE only needs to operate within this portion of the bandwidth configured by the system. The BWP also guarantees forward compatibility with the system, which can be user-defined in the BWP when the system needs to support new ports.

A terminal can be connected with up to four BWPS, uplink and downlink BWPS for FDD, respectively, and uplink–downlink paired BWPS for TDD (the central frequency points are the same, but the bandwidth and sub-carrier intervals can be different). The operation on BWP can be realized in three ways: high-level signaling configuration, physical downlink control channel (PDCCH) scheduling, and timer control. The following are four typical examples of BWP applications (Figs. 2.9–2.12).

Example 1: The terminal bandwidth (e.g., 20 MHz) is less than the whole system bandwidth (e.g., 100 MHZ).

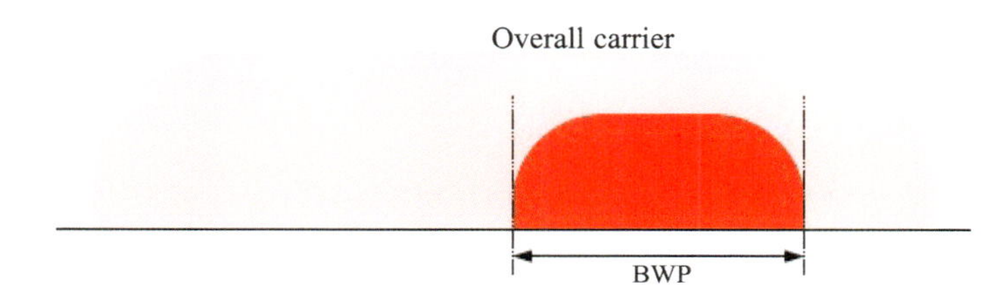

Figure 2.9 BWP Example 1.

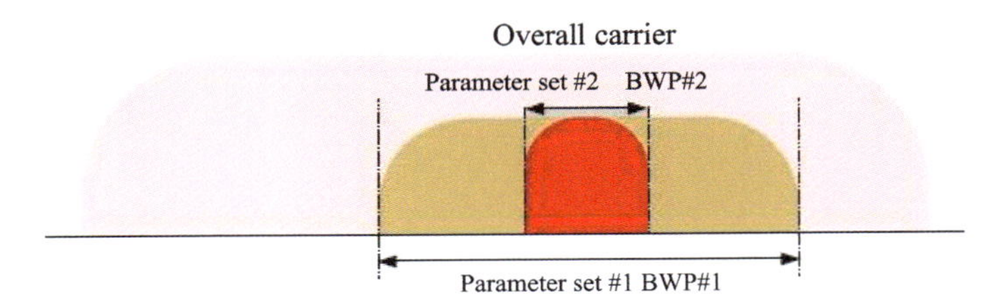

Figure 2.10 BWP Example 2.

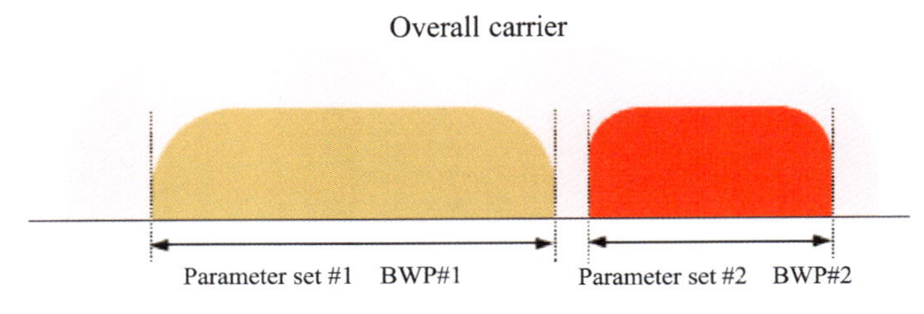

Figure 2.11 BWP Example 3.

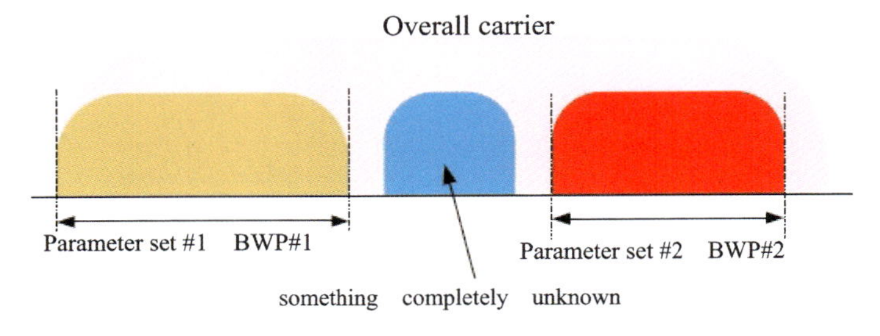

Figure 2.12 BWP Example 4.

Example 2: Conversion and adaption between BWP are done with different bandwidths to reduce UE power consumption under the premise of throughput variation.

Example 3: The open slot parameter set (numerology) can be transformed by switching BWP, e.g., from an outdoor high mobility small carrier interval to an indoor low mobility large carrier interval.

Example 4: The system carrier can support the existence of voids and flexible spectrum application scenarios.

To better support IoT, 5G defines NR Lite, which aims to support 100 Mb/s and 50 Mb/s downlink and uplink capabilities. The terminal battery life is 2–4 times longer than eMBB, with coverage capacity being 10–15 dB better than uRLLC. It can be used in fields, such as industrial wireless sensor networks, video surveillance, remote control of unmanned aerial vehicles, remote control of mechanical equipment, and wearable devices.

2.4 5G Key Technologies: Magic Tricks

5G key technology refers to the technologies that have not been adopted before or have been discussed while not used in scale, but have great benefits and are expected to be used for 5G network deployment and service capability achievement. Among them, massive MIMO serves as a 5G coverage multiplier and capacity multiplier to ensure the deployment of macro base stations for the bandwidth greater than 3.5 GHz. Millimeter-wave communication technology can enhance 5G service capacity and increase the possibility of widespread deployment. Given the importance of the Internet of Everything to industries and companies, technologies that emerged in the 4G era, such as micro base stations, integrated access and backhaul, and D2D, are likely to play a bigger role in the 5G era.

2.4.1 *Large-scale multiple antennas*

The innovation in the field of antenna conforms to the law of spiral rise as pain point-driven innovation. In the 2G era, in order to improve coverage, the base station side introduced a 2-port antenna supporting spatial diversity and polarization diversity, and the mobile phone side adopted a single antenna. In the 3G era, the 2-port antenna became the standard of the base station, and the mobile phone side adopted single-send with double-receive technology. From TD-SCDMA to LTE TDD, the 8-port smart antenna applied channel interoperability, which produced positive results in improving coverage and enhancing user experience. It becomes the standard and supports dual-user dual-streaming parallel transmission at most. FDD LTE also gradually adopts the 4-port base station to support single-user multi-streaming.

5G faces some unique problems. First of all, according to the theory of radio wave propagation, the higher the main frequency of 5G FR1/FR2, the greater the route loss will be and the shorter the covering distance will be under the equivalent isotropically radiated power (EIRP, i.e., the sum of antenna gain and transmitting power, commonly expressed as dBm). Theoretically, this could be compensated by increasing the number of antennas, but this would lead to an increase in RF channels and a sharp increase in costs, so the cost and performance must be balanced. Secondly, 5G must increase the capacity by more than three times. As traditional means such as physical layer coding, modulation, and scheduling technology have limited effects, increasing the number of antennas to realize space division multiplexing is the best choice.

At the end of 2010, Thomas at Bell Labs proposed the concept of 5G massive MIMO in wireless communications. Massive MIMO can also reduce the interference between users by using the approximate orthogonality of channels between different users and realize multi-user space division multiplexing. Massive MIMO is an extension of traditional MIMO technology. As shown in Fig. 2.13, the advantage of massive MIMO multi-user multiplexing lies in the fact that space resources can be fully utilized without base station splitting. Beamforming technology can concentrate the beam with minimal energy in a small area, thus the interference can be greatly suppressed. The key to ensuring the user's perception rate is to focus the signal intensity on the specific direction and the specific user group to realize reliable and high-speed signal transmission.

Specifically, the wide adoption of massive MIMO in 5G shows that in the sub-6 GHz frequency bands, 4G basically uses single column of antenna and 2T2R (2 transmitters, 2 receivers) RRU or two columns of antenna and 4T4R (4 transmitters, 4 receivers) RRU, which does not have multi-user space division multiplexing capability. In total, it supports not more than 4 streams, and has poor three-dimensional coverage and outdoor to indoor coverage. 5G adopts massive MIMO, which can support up to 16 streams,

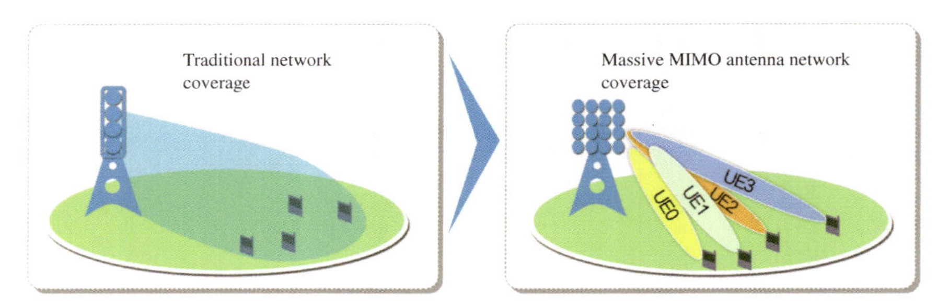

Figure 2.13 Comparison between traditional antenna system and massive MIMO antenna system.

significantly improving capacity and enhancing tall building coverage. The link loss of the MMW frequency band is relatively big. Array antenna is used for directional transmission in both base station and devices, which can improve the coverage ability of the MMW frequency band. It is expected that MMW can be deployed in both macro and micro stations.

Massive MIMO can be applied to the following scenarios:

(1) *Urban areas with dense population, CBDs, and stadiums*: There are a large number of users and large requirements for upstream and downstream capacity, and interference needs to be effectively suppressed.
(2) *No indoor distribution*: The O2I problem (i.e., indoor coverage problem) is solved through communication from outdoor to indoor.
(3) *Uplink restriction and SUL*: Its strong reception performance is employed.

Considering the fact that sub-6 GHz bandwidth commonly appears at 100 MHz level, digital beamforming (DBF) is often used to rapidly track the beam through channel reciprocity as well as to suppress the interference for the different users (Fig. 2.14). The beamforming is realized

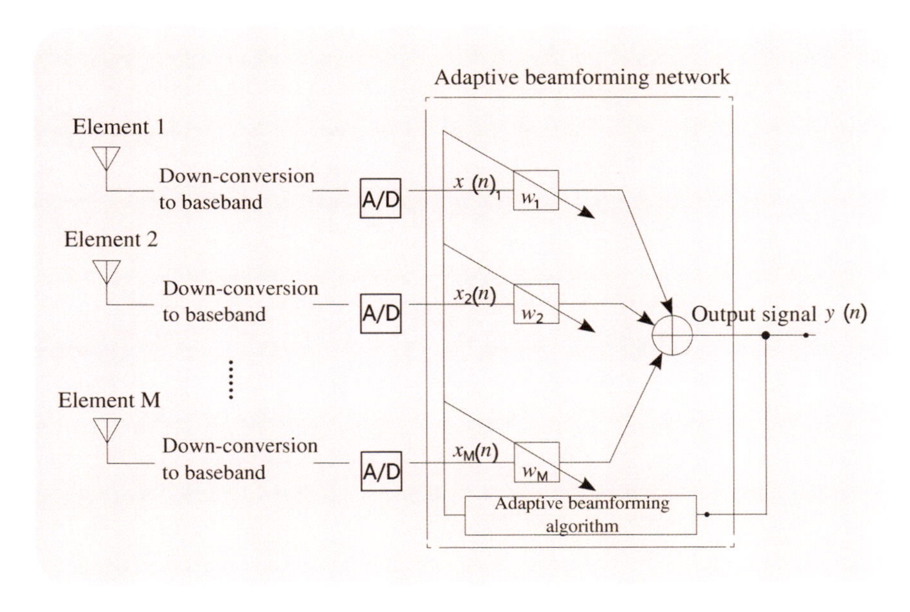

Figure 2.14 DBF Frame Adopted by sub-6 GHz.

through baseband weighting, and DBF needs to rely on very strict correction from baseband to antenna ports, which has high complexity and power consumption. As the bandwidth of millimeter waves is commonly at a few hundred MHz level, the digital processing complexity and power consumption are very high, so analog-dominant hybrid beamforming (HBF) is often used (Fig. 2.15). The beamforming is mainly RF phase shift (analog) with less baseband phase shift (digital). HBF also requires correction, and its price is the two-way alignment between base station and devices, so it needs some alignment time (between the magnitude from a few milliseconds to tens of milliseconds), which will sacrifice some mobility (i.e., poorer high-speed support ability). But considering that MMW is primarily extreme speed transmission, the sacrifice is worth it.

Although massive MIMO is widely used in the first 5G commercial deployments, there is still a lot of room for improvement in terms of power efficiency, multi-user pairing, mobile support, and small package service support.

2.4.2 *Millimeter-wave communication*

So far, there has been no successful case of millimeter-wave use in the field of civil mobile communication, although it has been

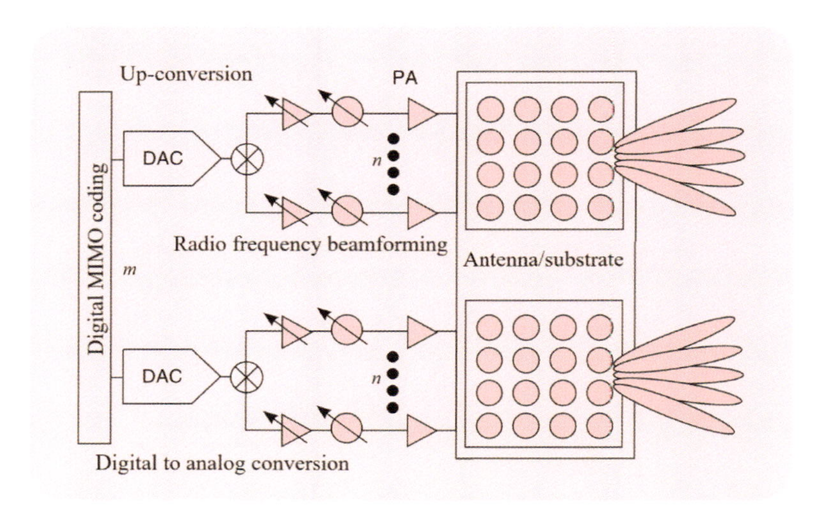

Figure 2.15 The millimeter wave adopts analog-based and digital-assisted frame (HBF frame).

pre-commercialized in the United States, South Korea, Hong Kong, and other countries or regions. At present, the successful practice of millimeter wave includes visual microwave transmission represented by 15 GHz/70 GHz, in which the Fresnel area must be free of occlusion in order to ensure the reliability of communication, the application of MMW satellite communication mainly due to the small loss in outer space and atmosphere layer, and short-range (within 100 m) automotive radar. Generally speaking, the advantages of millimeter-wave large bandwidth and high-resolution features are utilized under the premise of reliable information transmission.

Based on the above experience, small outdoor honeycomb, indoor, fixed wireless, and backhaul scenarios are undoubtedly the main battlefields of MMW. On the one hand, these scenarios have a manageable loss. On the other hand, space (such as multiple office areas) can be used to naturally isolate multi-user interference, construct frequency multiplexing, and improve spectral efficiency. At the same time, the large bandwidth of the millimeter wave can improve single-user experience by several times than that of C-band. Therefore, millimeter wave can be applied to the outdoor macro station scenario by increasing EIRP to make full use of outdoor strong emission and direct path for communication and effectively share the sub-6 GHz load.

As shown in Fig. 2.16, the core content of MMW communication first involves a two-way alignment of base station and device and then avoids interference as far as possible through the space–time frequency.

2.4.3 *Micro base station*

Before 4G, the micro base station is mainly applied in the digital indoor system (DIS), a small amount of outdoor blind area coverage and marginal network for universal service, which is small in scale and often only serves as a supplement to the large-power macro station. The main reason is that it is difficult to obtain the station site of a small power base station and its cost is more expensive. At the same time, the low-frequency macrocell can give a good balance between capacity and coverage, while the micro base station will lead to serious interference, and the limited spectrum makes it unable to avoid interference. It is at the beginning that 5G proposed the Ultra-Dense Network (UDN) built on the basis of micropower nodes (Fig. 2.17) as a measure of equal importance to spectrum acquisition and spectrum efficiency improvement.

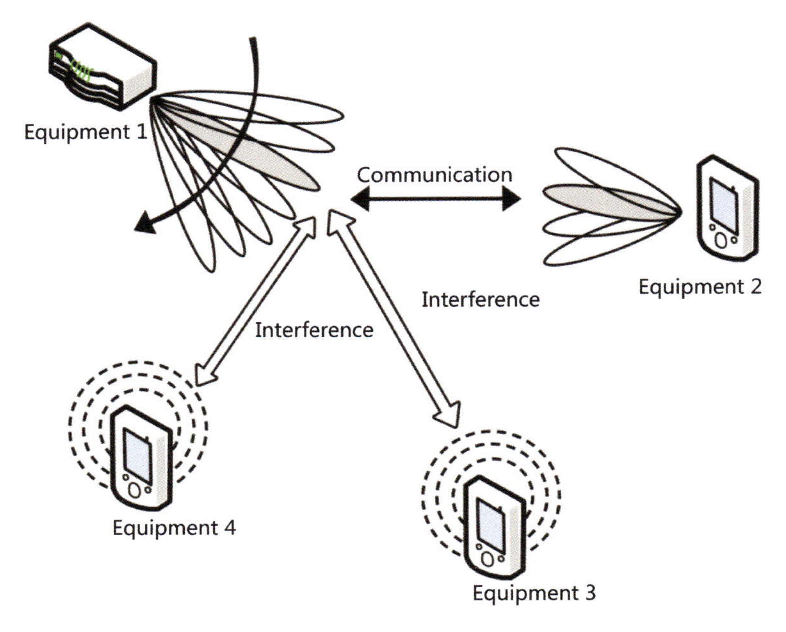

Figure 2.16 Schematic diagram of millimeter-wave communication and interference.

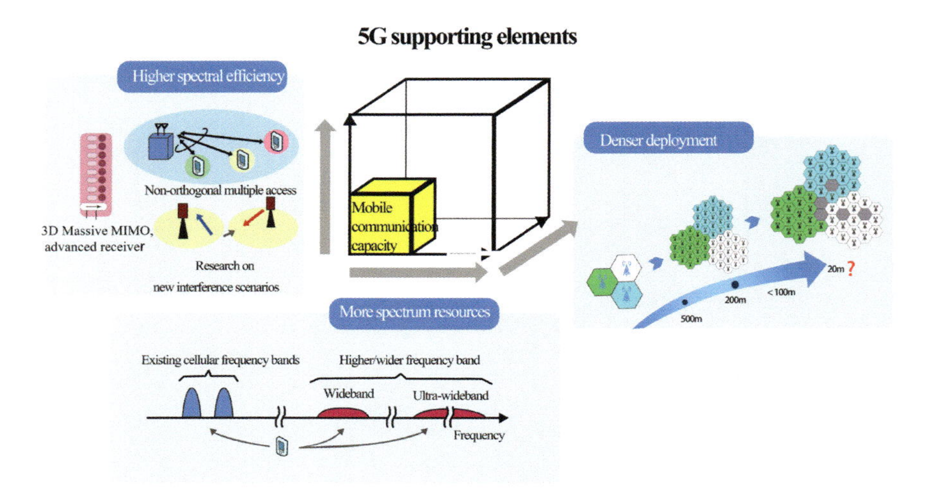

Figure 2.17 Significance of micro-power base station and dense networking.

The feasibility of 5G micro-power base station networking is improved, for the following reasons:

(1) 5G core frequency band is in the higher centimeter wave and millimeter-wave range, with small electromagnetic feature size, small physical size under the same array scale, and limited output power. The use of micro base stations is more economical and environmentally friendly, while a large bandwidth can ensure low cost per bit. In addition, the high-frequency band is abundant, providing better means to avoid interference and increase the feasibility of deploying UDN.
(2) Every country actively strives for the site resources including the light pole and promotes the multi-functional solution similar to the smart light pole, so that co-construction of 5G becomes possible, and communication costs per unit are reduced.
(3) 5G-enabling industries make it more likely for industries and enterprises to build their own networks or transfer site resources to entrust operators to do so, leading to a much higher likelihood of micro base station deployment for special scenarios.
(4) 5G openness also ensures the possibility of diversified network construction methods and the scenario of crowdfunding.

2.4.4 *Comprehensive access and backhaul*

Backhaul refers to the part with which the wireless access network is connected to the core network. It is now the dominant option of mobile network building. Optical fiber is the ideal choice for the backhaul network, but in the environment where the optical fiber is difficult to deploy or costs are high for deployment, point-to-point microwave and millimeter-wave backhaul, Wi-Fi backhaul, and even wireless mesh cascade backhaul are all possible alternatives. Although this increases the chance of flexible choice, the access and backhaul are rigid heterogeneous bindings, which not only makes equipment integration difficult but also results in suboptimal service quality. For these reasons, the 5G standards organization defined IAB, as shown in Fig. 2.18.

For the millimeter-wave era with dense micro stations, every lamppost in the city could be deployed with micro stations. IAB's use of the 5G frequency band, especially in millimeter frequency band, will integrate

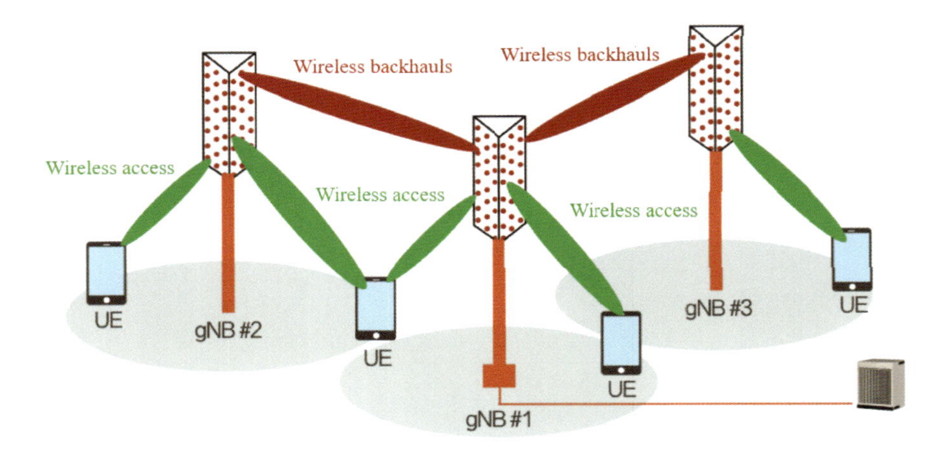

Figure 2.18 IAB schematic.

wireless access and backhaul, both of which use 5G protocols, and achieve more flexible, simple, and low-cost base station deployment through self-backhaul. So, the IAB makes 5G widespread deployment more likely and economical.

2.4.5 *Device to device*

Until now, mobile communications have been about trusted communication between network-based (especially base station) devices, such as mobile phones. This scenario will change in the 5G era. First, some 5G applications will show the characteristics of trusted adjacent communication, such as communication between IoT devices, represented by communication from car to car, car to person, and car to infrastructure. Second, there are coverage holes and communication blind areas in many 5G frequency bands, resulting in the feasibility of opportunistic communication. Third, enterprise and industry application scenarios have strong requirements to expand the coverage of communication. Finally, the devices have strong communication, storage, and computing capabilities. The above features bring into consideration the use of authorized and unauthorized frequency bands in D2D direct communication. D2D refers to allowing direct communication from one mobile device to another rather than via a base station.

Looking back upon history, D2D usage can be found in walkie-talkie and Wi-Fi peer to peer (P2P). LTE has also promoted D2D and is known as the LTE Proximity Services (ProSe) technology. It mainly includes the direct discovery function, i.e., the device which can detect whether there are directly connectable devices around or direct connection communication, which is the data interaction with the surrounding devices. In the 4G age, D2D is mainly applied in the field of public security. In the 5G era, the application scope of D2D communication is expected to expand due to the rise of IoT applications such as car networking, autonomous driving, and wearable devices. The biggest motivation may come from the fact that enterprises and industries will apply 5G D2D technology to the enterprise dedicated spectrum and the unlicensed spectrum. Therefore, relevant parties need to keep an open mind on the premise of controlling interference and explore various feasible ways of use.

2.5 Challenges and Countermeasures: Scaling New Heights

5G won't be easy. The smartphone will show its marginal effects, and IoT applications will take time. What follows is a list of issues that 5G must address in its subsequent standardization and application practices. 5G is an open system that will surely find opportunities in the midst of challenges.

2.5.1 *Information security*

Mobile communication has always attached importance to information security. GSM used the network based on SIM cards for terminal authentication, but this leads to the exposure of the International Mobile Subscriber Identification (IMSI) code, which results in fake base stations all over the streets. 4G adopts two-way authentication between the terminal and the network. In order to improve communication security and protect user privacy, the 5G network has developed a variety of network security mechanisms on the basis of 3G and 4G network security technologies, among which network slicing, multiple extensible authentication, and intelligent active defense are the three mechanisms that deserve the most attention and expectation.

2.5.1.1 *Network slicing*

Network slice security mechanisms can improve the flexibility, scalability, and deployment speed of the communication system. 5G network slicing is based on wireless access network, carrier network, and core network infrastructure, as well as a logic network facing different business characteristics with network virtualization technology. In addition to providing traditional mobile network security mechanisms (such as access authentication, access layer and non-access layer signaling security, data confidentiality, and integrity protection), network slicing security also needs to provide end-to-end security isolation mechanism between network slices to ensure that different application qualities are not affected by each other.

2.5.1.2 *Multiple extensible security mechanisms*

In the 5G era, mobile communication networks not only serve individual consumers but also more importantly serve different industries. The 5G era is not just about building faster mobile networks or developing more powerful smartphones but also about generating new types of services connecting the world, such as mMTC and uRLLC. In the 5G network, the traditional binary (base station and terminal) trust model will be integrated to build the multiple (base station, terminal and other core network elements) trust model, as shown in Fig. 2.19. Network and different industries can be combined with business identity management, so that business operation is more efficient, and users' personalized requirements can be met.

2.5.1.3 *Intelligent active defense and security mechanism*

5G is an open network, and massive IoT devices are outdoor with limited hardware resources, unattended and vulnerable to hacker attacks and control, which will expose them to a large number of network attacks. If the existing artificial defense mechanism is adopted, it will not only have a slow response speed but also lead to a sharp increase in defense cost. Therefore, it is necessary to consider using an intelligent mechanism to defend against security threats from massive IoT devices.

2.5.2 *Green and energy conservation*

5G power consumption needs to be viewed from two perspectives: terminal and base station.

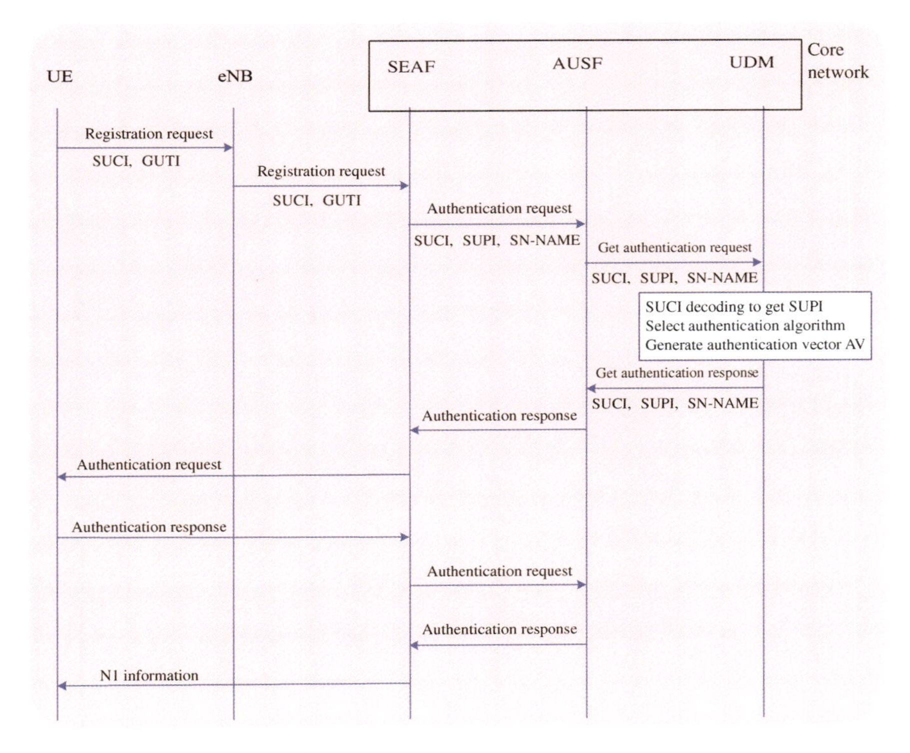

Figure 2.19 5G authentication process.

Note: SUCI, subscription concealed identifier, GUTI, globally unique temporary UE identity, SEAF, security anchor function, SUPI, subscription permanent identifier, SN-NAME, service network name.

From the terminal point of view, the battery capacity is increasing, and the daily use time of the user terminal is increasing, so the problem of energy-saving is very prominent. Before 4G, the terminal energy-saving benefits from the high integration of silicon-based processes in the baseband and RF channels and the power efficiency improvement of compound semiconductors in the front-end PA, as well as the characteristics of discontinuous transmission and reception. 5G needs to consider the power consumption data of different frequency bands and select appropriate ones for communication according to channel conditions. Given the traffic transmission requirements (unit in Gb/s), the power consumption of a certain frequency band is equal to the product of power and time length. When both millimeter wave and sub-6 GHz have good signal quality and meet the transmission conditions, the large bandwidth of millimeter wave can ensure that the given flow rate can be transmitted in less time. However, compared with sub-6 GHz, the power consumption of millimeter wave does not improve much, so there is a turning point. For example, when the millimeter-wave power consumption is twice that of C-band, it is energy-saving if the communication time of millimeter wave is less than two times of C-band. In fact, millimeter-wave communications last about a tenth as long as C-band, which means 80% less power. From the point of view of energy, millimeter wave is more energy-saving as long as the propagation conditions permit. The advantages of C-band are small and medium packets, in which case it is useless to force the choice of millimeter wave.

5G base stations fall into two categories: the first is traditional BBU+RRU distributed base stations, and the second is the high-level cutting architecture of CU+DU (including ARU). As shown in Fig. 2.20, the power consumption of the base station is mainly ARU (or RRU) and BBU. BBU is mainly responsible for baseband digital signal processing, such as fast Fourier transform (FFT)/inverse fast Fourier transform (IFFT), modulation/demodulation, and channel coding/decoding, which

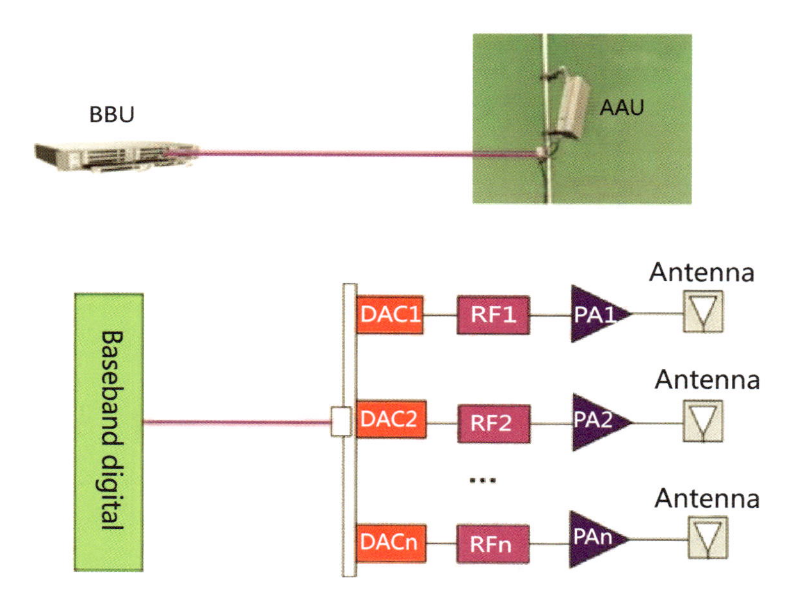

Figure 2.20 Base station architecture and its power consumption.

are mainly realized with application-specific integrated circuit (ASIC). Active antenna unit (AAU) is mainly composed of digital-to-analog conversion (DAC), radio frequency (RF), power amplifier (PA), and antenna unit, and other parts, which are mainly responsible for transforming the baseband digital signals into analog signals and then modulating them into high-frequency RF signals and launching out the antenna by amplifying PA for enough power.

From less channels in 4G to more channels in 5G massive MIMO (32 or 64 above), under the premise of the same output power, the main power consumption difference is that the increasing channels lead to sending and receiving frequency conversion, analog-to-digital converter (ADC) and DAC, digital pre-distortion (DPD), and CPRI/eCPRI parts. Different manufacturers would have different levels of 5G power consumption because of the different architecture and component technologies. Even so, the unit bit power consumption (B/J) of 5G still presents a downward trend compared with 4G, showing an overall energy-saving trend. The proposition of 5G energy-saving lies in two aspects: (1) considering the limited power capacity of a single station, 5G peak power consumption needs to be reduced; (2) considering that the service volume varies with time, 5G power consumption and energy-saving need to be dynamic. When the service volume drops, the 5G base station can adopt energy-saving measures in the carrier level, channel level, or time slot level.

2.5.3 *Open system*

The Open Radio Access Network (ORAN) Alliance is a global operator initiative that aims to make the next generation of wireless access networks more open and intelligent than previous generations. The key to the reference design developed by the ORAN Alliance is the relevant virtualized network elements with open and standardized interfaces, and the white box technology from open source will become an important support for these reference designs. The goal of ORAN is to break the monopoly of traditional segmented manufacturers in the RAN market, further reduce the network construction cost and improve operational efficiency.

There is no doubt that ORAN is flexible in terms of business provision and strategy adjustment, and has advantages in small capacity and small scope coverage scenarios. ORAN can meet the requirements of the enterprise industry for high customization, self-control, and rapid business launch. At the same time, it must be clearly recognized that the ORAN architecture, with its heavy use of general-purpose hardware and software, has the following problems: coverage, capacity, and power consumption cannot keep up with the dedicated vertically integrated RAN. The overall balance of performance (such as capacity, coverage, networking, and mobility) has not been fully validated. General hardware leads to high power consumption. Equipment from different manufacturers leads to high maintenance costs for operators, which may be the opposite of ORAN's original intention.

In addition, Wi-Fi 6 and subsequent Wi-Fi 7 draw on the experience of LTE and NR resource management and make great progress in networking and customer experience, which will also become an important part of the 5G open system.

In general, for an evolving open technology system like ORAN and Wi-Fi 6, the best choice must be made according to the business requirements, spectrum status, and the requirements of business entities (operators, enterprises).

2.5.4 *Prospects*

As the factor resources such as engine, energy, chemical industry, machinery, as well as road fully contribute to the development of car, in the 5G era, mobile communication and Big Data, artificial intelligence, and automatic control will form the generalized 5G or 5G+, and the unknown part of 5G will be more than the known. 5G will create value for the whole society through continuous efforts. As China Mobile envisions, "In 5G development, network is the foundation, fusion is the key, cooperation is the trend and application is the fundamentality".

As mentioned above, 5G is not only a communication technology but also an important carrier, which will bring great changes to human life and the whole society. We cannot help but be curious of the times when 5G will meet manufacturing, transportation, medical treatment, and home, and imagine what kind of a wonderful story would happen then.

Chapter 3

Magic Enabling of 5G: Tremendous Social Shift Empowering Human Life

3.1 5G Promotes Social Change

If 4G has greatly changed our way of life, the upcoming 5G era will bring us a "high-speed, wide-connection, low-latency" web experience. Apart from that, it will also provide a network foundation for applications such as high-definition broadcasts, virtual reality (VR), telemedicine, unmanned vehicles, artificial intelligence, and smart city, promoting the whole society into the age of "Internet of Everything". Going forward, the 5G era will serve as the information digitalization age in which the whole human society will be changed. In the 5G era, traditional industrial powers will not necessarily remain strong, while emerging countries have more development opportunities. It is easy to imagine that, with the popularization of 5G commercial applications, lives in the future will be just similar to that presented in science fiction movies, reflecting intelligence and convenience everywhere.

3.1.1 *5G enables innovation in the new era*

With the progressive development of 5G technology, the world will gradually enter an era of Big Data explosion, which is a revolutionary change, among which the most critical is a radical transformation that happened in the system network architecture. Different from the inter-personal communication supported by 1G to 4G technologies, 5G will provide communication technology support for an intelligent connection between people, people and things, and among things. As the foundation of communication, 5G leads the overall innovation of network technology and opens a new era of Internet development through the combination of various modes, such as cloud, virtualization, and Internet.

With the launch of commercial 5G, human society will enter a brand-new era of intelligent Internet, in which technologies such as mobile Internet, artificial intelligence, and Big Data fuse together. In the Internet system based on 5G, since mobile connectivity breaks through the limitation of the traditional bandwidth, time delay and a large number of terminal access problems get solved fundamentally, giving full play to the advantages of intelligence, Big Data and artificial intelligence, as well as any new business model and service model creating a lot of new opportunities, which are important forces in the future growth.

The deployment of new application scenarios can be achieved by the 5G mobile communication network, such as car networking, Internet of Everything, and large data centers. At the same time, 5G can also have full application and development in emerging areas, such as smart medicine, smart city, smart home, and smart creation, comprehensively improving the level of social informatization and economic activity.

Compared to the traditional Internet, 5G features Internet of Everything. In the future, with a large number of intelligent hardware connected to the 5G mobile communication network, the number of devices connected will increase from hundreds of millions or billions to tens of billions, which will definitely bring about the explosion of the Internet of Everything market.

Resting on the growth of 5G communication technology, new technologies and applications that are being derived from all walks of life will become the primary driving force and direction to promote social and economic development. The deep fusion of 5G with the real economy will become a fulcrum supporting the transformation of traditional industries and aiding emerging industries in building core competitiveness. It will have a profound impact on accelerating the digitization, networking, and intelligent transformation of industries as well as fostering new applications, new models, and new business forms.

3.1.2 *5G improves new intelligent industries*

High-speed mobile Internet was produced with 4G technology, which gave rise to the large-scale development and popularization of data services, such as cloud computing, mobile social network, and mobile multimedia. 5G is the key to the digital transformation of all industries in the future, in which the information transmission rate and the number of devices connected will increase at multiple levels on the existing basis with significantly reduced transmission delay. At the same time, communication service providers can provide more reliable communication services for individual users, enterprises, and governments with the 5G technology. The information industry and traditional processing and manufacturing industries will face fully reconstituted transformation, resulting in a new industrial pattern, as shown in Fig. 3.1. Moreover, the value of 5G technology will be finally realized through the innovation of the vertical industry.

3.1.2.1 *Intelligent creation*

In intelligent creation, the vigorous development of 5G can speed up the transformation from traditional manufacturing to intelligent manufacturing, among which Internet of Everything, wireless automation control, logistics traceability, and industrial Augmented Reality (AR) application are involved in key applications. As the key technology used to connect people, machines, and devices, Internet of Everything can be greatly promoted by 5G technology in its application, which can play a

Figure 3.1 Application areas of 5G.

decisive role in promoting the intelligent transformation of factories. The adoption of 5G technology can realize wireless automatic control based on the distributed network, promote the effective management of production lines in modern factories, and expand the coverage of effective management. Features of 5G technology, such as wide coverage, low power consumption, and large connection, can be applied to logistics traceability to ensure that the whole production process of products can be tracked, thus realizing the automatic connection of the product life cycle. Industrial AR can better carry out production process monitoring, task assignment, and expert remote business through the support of 5G technology.

3.1.2.2 *Intelligent medicine*

5G technology plays an extremely important role in establishing a systematic, intelligent, and refined comprehensive medical and health supervision system, thus opening a new era of medical development. The technological change generated by 5G will have a profound impact on the entire medical and health industry, and improve the efficiency of medical treatment. Medical scenarios such as remote surgery, monitoring, and treatment may come true in the future.

3.1.2.3 *Intelligent transportation*

More breakthroughs on the Internet of Vehicles and autonomous driving will be realized due to the arrival of 5G commercial applications, opening up more imagination space for the whole industry. With 5G technology's advantages of high speed, large capacity, low delay, and high reliability, vehicle networking can not only help vehicles communicate with each other about location, speed, driving direction, and driving intention but also use roadside facilities to assist vehicles in perceiving the environment. 5G and vehicle networking technologies provide necessary technical support for the realization of autonomous driving. They can improve the environmental awareness of autonomous vehicles; moreover, they can achieve wireless connectivity between vehicles, enabling multiple vehicles to make collaborative decisions. They can then make reasonable action plans to forward the development of safe and autonomous driving of vehicles.

3.1.2.4 *Intelligent home*

The advantages of 5G technology can inject new and ample momentum into the development of the home Internet of Everything market. The application of 5G-based Internet of Everything in a intelligent home can not only significantly shorten the response time of home-to-home interconnection, step up user perception speed but also reduce the proportion of system business transmission resources and operating costs. Combining 5G technology with intelligent home meets the consumers' demands for a intelligent home environment, energy-saving, environmental protection, health and comfort, and speeds up the arrival of the intelligent home era.

3.1.2.5 *The game industry*

5G network provides data service with high speed and low delay. The bandwidth up to Gb/s can not only satisfy the transmission of games with full high-definition resolution but also realize 4K or even 8K level of game screens on mobile phones. The millisecond delay of a single digit is enough for any device to complete the interaction with the server in an instant. Based on high speed, 5G forwards the faster development of AR and VR, and promotes the rise of cloud games. Also, we can envisage more games, such as melee of the Thousand, real-time AR games, and ultra-HD wireless VR transmission, which will become reality one day. In the 5G era, the game industry will undoubtedly usher in a new revolutionary wave and at that time, cloud games and multiplayer ultra-HD games will become a reality.

3.1.2.6 *Smart finance*

In the 5G era, the transition from fintech to smart finance will be realized. Smart finance is not only a horizontal overlay of products but also provides more differentiated financial services and optimizes the products from the perspective of customers. Digital and intelligent banking 3.0 era is coming, which will drastically lead to changes of banks in the service mode, marketing mode, risk control mode, and operation mode, expand the service boundary of banks and finally change the business growth curve of banks.

The successful implementation of the 5G strategy can improve a country's communication capability. Furthermore, it can bring unprecedented development opportunities to the whole digital industry. Taking 5G construction as an opportunity, the development of related industries in China can boost the upstream electronic information manufacturing, the downstream digital vertical industry application, as well as the soft power of AI, Big Data, cloud computing, and other technologies which will become another source of driving national economic growth.

3.2 5G Helps the Evolution of Vertical Industries

3.2.1 *5G helps improve the productivity of the manufacturing sector*

Starting from the 21st century, we have been approaching an era of intelligence gradually, in which new technologies represented by the Internet, Big Data, cloud computing, and Internet of Everything have emerged. Deeply integrated with every link in the manufacturing process, 5G will produce historic development opportunities for the transformation and upgrading of the manufacturing industry. With speed comparable to the transmission speed of the fiber, all connections in Internet of Everything and real-time ability came close to the industrial bus, while the rapid development of 5G fully aligned with the traditional manufacturing intelligent transformation's demands for the application of wireless network. 5G has gradually penetrated into the industrial sector, triggering a series of application integration, innovation, and change, and traditional manufacturing will once again usher in a new upgrade direction — smart creation.

3.2.1.1 *Smart creation*

The manufacturing industry plays a vital role at the national level and even in the whole human society. Manufacturing has been listed as a priority in many countries' industrial upgrading plans. Major countries in the world have made long-term plans and deployed them for the intelligent development of the manufacturing industry, such as China's "Made in China 2025", Germany's "Industry 4.0 Platform", and the US's "Industrial Internet Plan", showing that smart creation has become a national strategic topic and a global topic.

In a broad sense, smart creation is defined as the general term for the advanced manufacturing process, system, and mode equipped with functions such as information perception acquisition, intelligent judgment and decision-making, and automatic execution, which are based on the new generation of information technology through all aspects of manufacturing activities, such as design, production, management, and service. Compared to traditional manufacturing, the advantages of smart creation can be roughly summarized into five aspects: (1) having a keen self-discipline, perception and understanding of the environment, and their own information and then planning the system's own behavior after analysis and judgment in a targeted manner; (2) obvious features of man–machine integration, deep integration of human intelligence and machine intelligence, highlighting the core position of human beings in the smart creation system and better realization of potential under the assistance of an intelligent machine; (3) numerous virtual reality technologies, integration of computer and signal processing, animation skills, and multimedia simulation technology, with the help of a variety of image and sound sensors, simulation of product manufacturing process and final product state; (4) with self-organization and ultra-fusion, smart creation units can conform to the requirements of the production task self-group, and at the same time, the component units have certain fusion ability in the operation mode and structure form; (5) with strong learning and resilience ability and deep use of artificial intelligence, a smart creation system can continuously achieve self-learning in the production practice and apply the "knowledge" gained to the manufacturing process, while at the same time updating "knowledge" based on the feedback from practice and having the ability of self-diagnosis, troubleshooting, and functional recovery.

Through the self-organizing flexible manufacturing system, smart creation can achieve efficient and personalized production goals. Its carrier is the intelligent factory, its core is the intelligence of the key manufacturing link, its foundation is the end-to-end data flow, and its support is the information communication network. It does show that information communication system plays a key role in smart creation. In the process of smart creation, it needs to introduce highly reliable wireless communication technology for real-time communication between a large number of sensors, artificial intelligence platform, and human–machine interface under different network environments. 5G provides such a possibility, so it is also bound to become a key technology to promote the development of smart creation.

3.2.1.2 *5G contributes to the development of smart creation*

(1) *Industrial AR/VR technology*: In the future, the smart creation process will still be people-centered and exert the important role of human beings. But, intelligent factories will be highly flexible and versatile, which will put higher demands on the factory employees. AR/VR will have an irreplaceable role in improving product quality and production efficiency in order to better adapt to the intelligent process, as shown in Fig. 3.2.

In smart creation, AR equipment can be used to monitor the production process, guide the distribution of production tasks, provide remote expert technical support and remote equipment maintenance. VR technology, on the other hand, can simulate the entire production process and conduct a virtual evaluation before product manufacturing in order to find the possible problems of the products as soon as possible, improve manufacturing efficiency and reduce manufacturing costs. In actual industrial manufacturing, AR/VR equipment usually needs to be flexible and portable, so the information processing is carried out in the cloud, and information transmission is realized with AR/VR equipment through wireless means. At the same time, AR/VR equipment can also obtain other necessary information

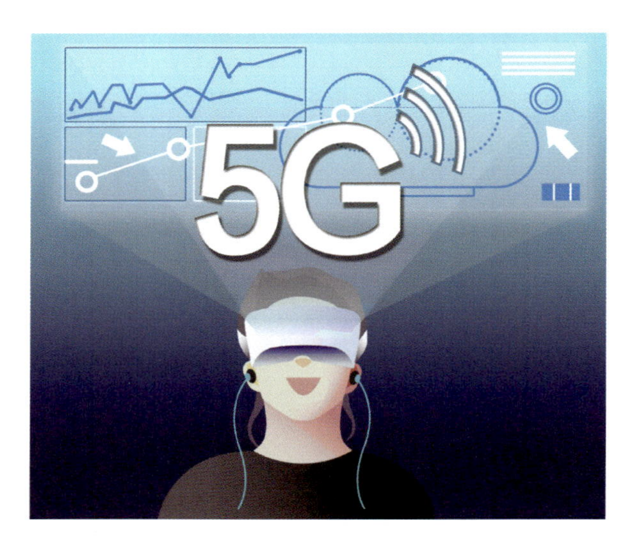

Figure 3.2 VR's role in the production process.

through the network, such as production environment data, production equipment data, and fault-handling guidance information.

The current 4G LTE network cannot provide the upload/download rate of high-resolution and high-bit-rate panoramic video required by AR/VR devices nor can it meet the low-latency requirements of AR/VR devices. But the high rate provided by 5G can fully support HD image and video transmission, which will comprehensively improve users' immersive experience. At the same time, 5G base stations with wider distribution and denser coverage can greatly reduce the transmission delay of AR/VR devices in the system, so as to reduce the vertigo generated in use and bring people the best viewing experience.

(2) *Industrial wireless automatic control*: Industrial wireless automatic control is the most basic mode of production in manufacturing plants, the core of which is the closed-loop control system. During the system control cycle, each sensor will be continuously measured, and the measured data will be fed back to the controller to adjust the actuator settings. The typical closed-loop control process cycle is as low as a millisecond, so the information transmission cycle of the system also needs to reach a millisecond to ensure the effectiveness and accuracy of the closed-loop control system, so as to avoid the huge loss led by control information error caused by time delay.

In the future smart creation system, the number of sensors will be extremely large in order to ensure more refined and automated operations, thus bringing forth certain challenges to the system's connectivity and data transmission delay. 5G end-to-end network slicing technology integrating various new technologies will be adopted to dynamically allocate network resources on the basis of different needs, create corresponding network slicing, optimize required network characteristics, and provide low latency, high reliability and mass connection network, making it possible to realize closed-loop control through the wireless network.

(3) *Industrial cloud-based robots*: In the process of smart creation, the application of robots will become more intelligent and diversified, which requires robots to have self-grouping cooperation ability to meet the requirements of flexible production. Therefore, cloud-based robots emerge as the times require. Compared to traditional robots, cloud-based robots connect to the cloud through the network and use the computer platform, Big Data, and artificial intelligence to

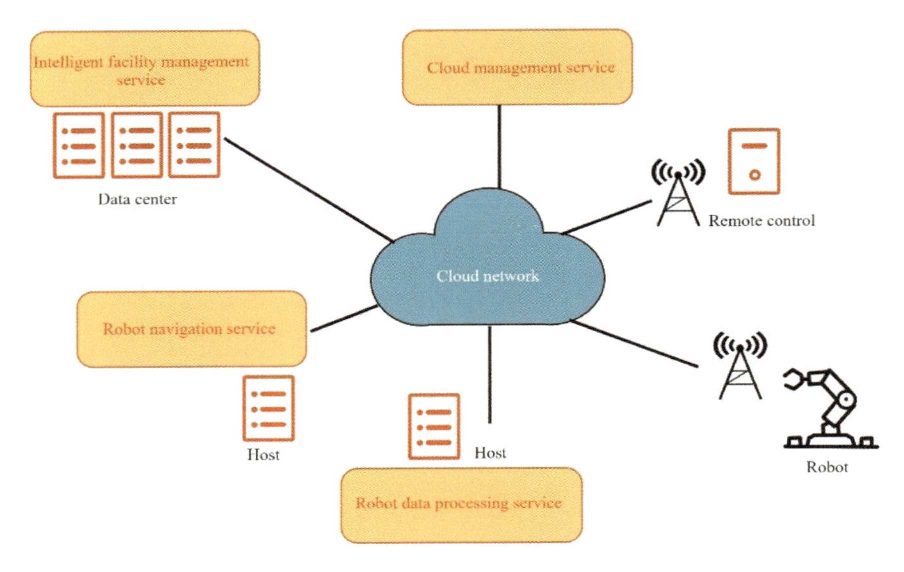

Figure 3.3 Framework of 5G-based cloud robot operation.

accurately calculate and optimize the manufacturing process, so as to achieve efficient collaborative work between high-performance computing systems and robot services, as shown in Fig. 3.3. In this way, the cost and energy consumption of the robot will be greatly reduced.

In the cloud and upgrade process of robots, low latency and highly reliable wireless communication network will be the key link. 5G slicing network can offer efficient end-to-end network support for cloud-based robots in smart creation, achieve delay as low as 1 ms, support 99.999% of highly reliable connections, satisfy the demand of cloud-based robots for delay and reliability, and provide effective technical support for the application of cloud-based robots.

3.2.1.3 *Summary and prospects*

The comprehensive outbreak of intelligent Internet in the 5G era has provided new opportunities for traditional manufacturing industries. By leveraging the characteristics of 5G communication technology, such as low delay and high reliability, industrial AR/VR technology, industrial wireless automatic control, and industrial cloud-based robot are applied to the industries, which significantly promotes the development of smart creation. In the 5G era, unmanned workshops will become the regular mode of production for manufacturers, and smart factories will gradually replace cheap labor. "Industry 4.0" in the 5G era is undoubtedly another earthshaking industrial revolution.

3.2.2 *5G facilitates the development of the healthcare industry*

3.2.2.1 *The dilemma of traditional medicine*

With the continuous progress of science and technology, the Chinese demand for improving the quality of life is constantly increasing, and the demand for medical treatment is also growing, thus making the medical institutions in our country a little undersupplied. In addition, medical resources are mainly distributed in big cities, resulting in a greater difficulty in getting medical treatment in places other than the big cities. The core problem of the difficulty lies in the contradiction between supply and demand. It is a reality that the total amount of medical and health resources in China is insufficient and the structure is unreasonable. The difficulty of getting medical treatment is not to be generalized. "Difficulty" is mainly reflected in that of getting medical treatment in large grade-A hospitals in big cities such as Beijing, Shanghai, and Guangzhou, including the affiliated hospitals of famous universities. Medical resources are insufficient and unbalanced, accounting for a long waiting time for registration in large hospitals. Moreover, expert registration is even more difficult to obtain, however, scalpers leverage this to make profits, causing an imperative medical reform (Fig. 3.4).

At present, the deficiency of medical resources in total, the uneven distribution, and the large gap in medical personnel make Chinese health development lag behind its economic development. The vast majority of medical resources in China are concentrated in cities, while the medical resources in cities are mainly concentrated in large hospitals. As shown in Fig. 3.5, the number of non-grade hospitals in China is the largest, but the number of patients is far less than that of tertiary hospitals, which have the least number of patients. The medical resources of urban central regional hospitals are firmly occupied by patients with minor and common diseases, so such hospitals are overcrowded, which is also the main reason for "difficult and expensive medical treatment" and long waiting times.

Figure 3.4 Hospital registration chaos.

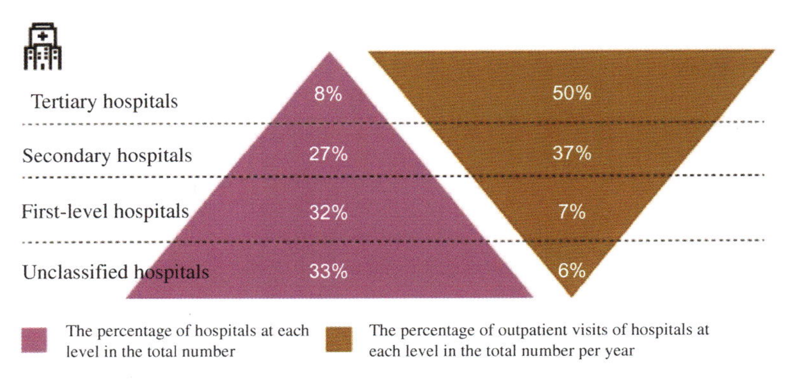

Figure 3.5 Ratio of the number of hospitals at each level and number of outpatient visits.

3.2.2.2 *5G contributes to changes in the healthcare industry*

5G technology is characterized by high speed, low time delay, and wide connections, making it a hot application in various industries. We can imagine that after 5G is integrated into the medical industry, the combination of Internet and medical treatment will bring a revolutionary storm to the medical industry in the following ways:

(1) We can complete the diagnosis and treatment without leaving the house. 5G technology will promote the rapid development of smart medicine on the Internet, enabling patients to find medical resources provided by various experts through an Internet search at home, find doctors suitable for their conditions according to their own symptoms and guide medical treatment through an artificial intelligence platform. The specific process is shown in Fig. 3.6.

(2) The efficiency of medical treatment is greatly enhanced. 5G technology will further enhance the efficiency of medical services and strengthen the information connection between patients and hospitals. Patients can quickly complete these steps by face recognition technology before registration and other medical treatments without the hassle of queuing. With high-speed transmission of 5G, medical staff can grasp vital signs data, imaging examination results, health records, and other relevant data of patients before diagnosis and

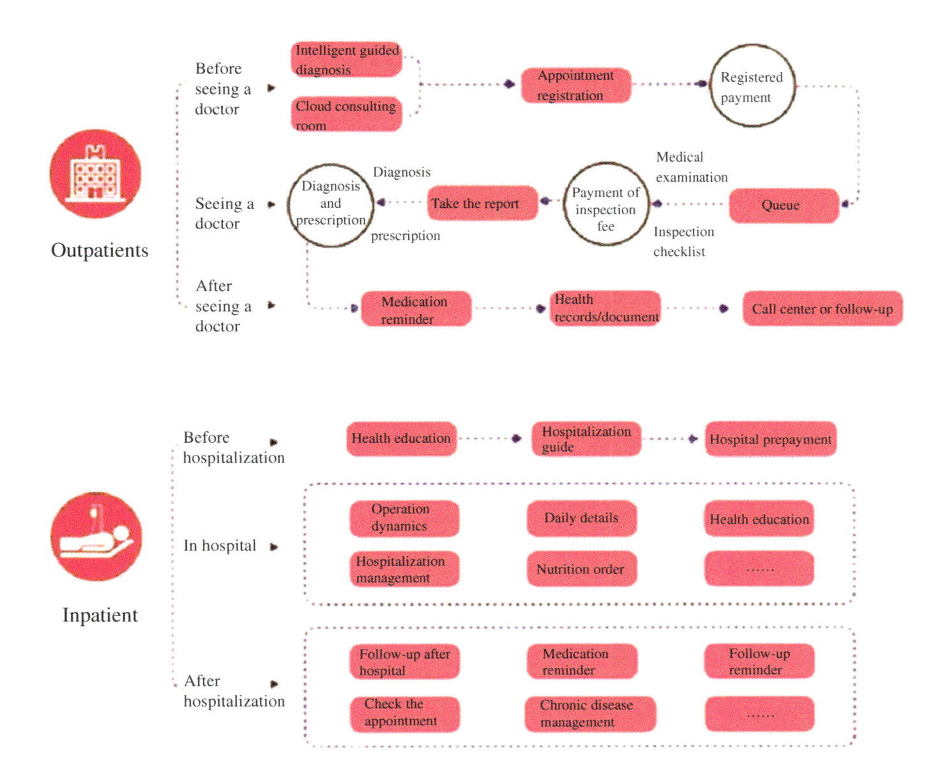

Figure 3.6 Medical treatment process in a modern hospital.

treatment, dramatically reducing the time for medical treatment. Remote diagnosis and treatment and even surgery can improve the utilization rate of high-quality medical resources and provide more patients with much-needed medical services.

3.2.2.3 *Efforts needed to develop 5G medical treatment*

Although 5G healthcare has begun to benefit people, there are still many restrictions on its promotion. Some of these are outlined as follows:

(1) *Cost*: The millimeter wave used by 5G has disadvantages such as poor penetration, large signal attenuation, small coverage area, and it's easy to be blocked. Therefore, to achieve full coverage of 5G signal in large hospitals, it is often necessary to build thousands of indoor base stations, costing more than one billion Yuan, which does not include the construction of outdoor signal base stations. In remote areas where communication infrastructure is poor, the cost is doubled. "Sky-high construction fee" is the primary obstacle to the promotion and development of 5G medical treatment.
(2) *Legal aspects*: 5G medical treatment will also generate a lot of legal problems. For example, once there is a medical accident in remote surgery, the mechanism of responsibility division is not clear, and the National Health Commission also reminds that remote surgery has certain risks: "scientific and prudent exploration should be conducted based on the current network technology and laws in medical science".
(3) *Other aspects*: There are still some problems to be solved in the development of 5G medical care. For example, the 5G medical and health standard system has not been established and improved. There is no unified standard for access mode and data format of terminal equipment. Moreover, the huge amount of data can cause a security risk, so 5G medical development still has a long way to go.

3.2.3 ***5G assists the intelligent evolution of urban traffic***

3.2.3.1 *The necessity of smart transportation development*

Since the reform and opening up, China's transportation industry has been developing rapidly, all of which cannot be separated from the government's great investment in transportation. The industrious Chinese have made China's infrastructure stand out in the world with their own hands. The Qinghai–Tibet Railway, the Hong Kong–Zhuhai–Macao Bridge, the Beijing Daxing International Airport, and other extremely difficult projects have all been conquered one by one. We are the world's "superhuman infrastructure".

In recent years, with the development of China's urbanization process and quick growth, the number of vehicles on urban roads is increasing, and all kinds of traffic problems have emerged, which put enormous pressure on the economic development. The traffic problems mentioned above mainly include the primary problem of traffic jams which became a big problem affecting city dwellers, the number of traffic accidents on the rise, and carbon exhaust from motor vehicles which became the main source of air pollution in cities. The development of smart transportation can ensure traffic safety, alleviate congestion problems, and reduce traffic accidents. According to the analysis, smart transportation can reduce the vehicle accident rate by more than 20%. There was a decrease in the number of deaths caused by traffic accidents by 30–70% each year; a decrease was also seen in the rate of traffic congestion by about 60%; there was an improvement in short-haul transport efficiency by nearly 70%; there was also an increase in the capacity of the existing road network by two to three times. In addition, the development of smart transportation can improve the operating efficiency of vehicles and roads as well as promote energy conservation and emission reduction. When a vehicle travels in the smart transportation system, the number of stops can be reduced by 30%, driving time can be cut down by 13–45%, and the vehicle's use efficiency can be increased by more than 50%, thus reducing fuel consumption and exhaust emission. Car fuel consumption could also be cut by 15% according to the analysis. It is inevitable and urgent for China to develop smart transportation.

3.2.3.2 *5G's impact on the development of smart transportation*

Due to the continuous development of 5G technology, there will be an era of "human–vehicle–road–network–cloud" five-dimensional collaborative development of vehicle networking (Fig. 3.7), which will have a very profound impact on traffic.

(1) *More comprehensive traffic information*: The rapid development of Internet of Everything will achieve more than transportation and

Figure 3.7 Collaborative development of vehicle network in five dimensions: "human–vehicle–road–network–cloud".

media, such as the weather system in vehicles, information about traffic poles and streetlights, people wearing automatic interconnection equipment, making the source of the traffic information wider, people's travel choice of vehicle type, fuel consumption, driving route along the way, information about the air quality, number of intersections, and traffic lights, and other relevant information.

(2) *More timely traffic information*: With the development of information technology and the innovation of transmission technology, the transmission of traffic information becomes more rapid. In the process of driving, in addition to the automatic detection of the surrounding environment and timely responses, in order to realize safe driving, vehicles can also receive traffic information from 10 km in front and 1 km behind, such as relevant interval average vehicle speed, time in seconds for the green light at the next crossing ahead, thus helping the vehicles choose the corresponding driving style and driving speed based on the road condition and matching the current traffic environment.

(3) *More intelligent transportation choices*: The mature application of AI and Big Data technology, coupled with a powerful smart transportation management platform, makes the system more familiar with travel behavior and preferences, and facilitates the automatic planning of travel plans for users. Meanwhile, the system can provide a variety of alternative traffic schemes based on the traffic conditions around the travel transfer node. For example, after arriving at a city for the first time, people can receive different transportation schemes recommended by the system on the basis of the current traffic conditions (such as taxi, subway, and self-driving), corresponding routes, and time-related costs after getting off the plane, so that people can choose independently and realize low-carbon travel, green life, and sustainable development.

(4) *More scientific traffic management decisions*: The complete network of transportation facilities and the complete collection of traffic information make the traffic information data more comprehensive. Through in-depth analysis and modeling of traffic information data, traffic scheduling and planning will be more scientific. Traffic Big Data can be applied in simulation analysis, ranging from the relief of road congestion and the optimization of traffic light signal length to the adjustment of bus routes and the construction of traffic trunk roads. Moreover, real-time traffic flow monitoring can be implemented in emergencies and major celebrations, and changes in traffic flow can be deduced to provide emergency management and control in advance.

3.2.3.3 *Future prospects*

Let's imagine being woken up by an intelligent speaker one morning in the future. It will tell you today is sunny and hence an appropriate day to travel for an outing, following which you brush your teeth in front of the mirror which lists several surroundings for the outing destination. After you choose the right destination, the mirror will send the information automatically to the vehicle navigation system. Then, the vehicle navigation system will have a series of accurate estimations, which will guide you through an intelligent speaker what time to go out and which is the most convenient way. It is cool to think about it, right? In fact, this is just one aspect of travel information query and planning. It is believed that many intelligent transportation modes will become more and more popular with the application of 5G technology.

3.2.4 *5G facilitates the process of smart home*

3.2.4.1 *The current situation of smart home*

With the increasing popularity of smart homes worldwide, people have a strong feeling that it will bring all kinds of convenience for life, and the appearance of smart home fundamentally improves the quality of home life. The smart home takes the house as the main carrier and uses network communication technology and automatic control technology to connect the communication equipment, household appliances, and family security devices related to home life to an intelligent system. This system can achieve centralized or remote monitoring and control. It forms efficient residential facilities and family schedule management system, maintains the coordination of these home facilities and residential environment and improves home safety and also makes the environment convenient, comfortable, and artistic.

3.2.4.2 *5G contributes to the leapfrog development of smart home*

In the era of the 5G smart home, 5G mobile broadband entry becomes possible. It can replace the conventional fixed-line broadband fiber access and carry out whole-house wireless network coverage, coming up with more convenient information acquisition methods for family members. At the same time, 5G features high speed and low latency, which can provide a smoother connection and a better user experience.

(1) *The fusion of 5G and ultra-HD TV*: People are always looking for higher-quality video and audio experiences for better immersion. In recent years, the size of a flat-panel TV is getting larger and larger, which needs to match with the higher display resolution. Meanwhile, the market needs a clearer and more realistic flat-panel TV with a stronger sense of presence. Therefore, an 8K ultra-HD TV with a display resolution of 7680 pixels × 3840 pixels is introduced. With a display resolution of 33.178 megapixels and frame per second of 30 f/s, the uncompressed bit rate of 8K video at the entry level is up to 30 Gb/s. Even with the most advanced coding compression technology H. 265 or AVS2, the transmission bit rate of 8K video at the entry level is only 100 Mb/s, so it requires strong network transmission capacity. The ultra-high bandwidth and ultra-low delay of the 5G network will provide effective technical support for 8K video transmission in the future. The high flow rate and large flow in the 5G era will promote the development of ultra-HD video with higher quality.

    5G 8K smart TV will be the product of 5G and 8K ultra-HD TV. It is an 8K TV with integrated 5G functions, as shown in Fig. 3.8. Its peak bandwidth is above 1 Gb/s and even up to 10 Gb/s, and the fast download of 8K videos can be realized. A 150 GB 8K movie can be downloaded only in 60 s and watching an 8K video broadcast is no longer a problem. Watching football matches at home may turn out to be a better experience than watching them live. It supports massive

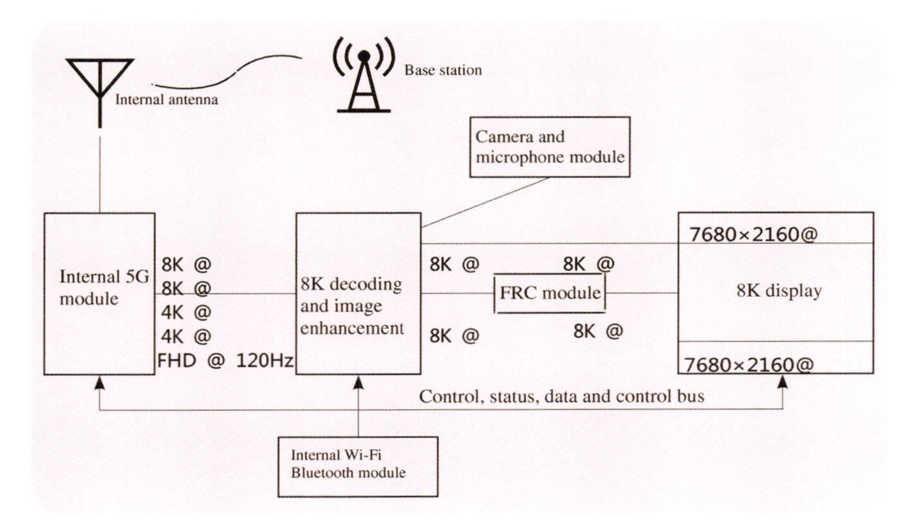

Figure 3.8 5G 8K smart TV frame.

Note: FRC: Frame Rate converter.

IoT device access and the number of IoT connected devices per square meter is up to 10,000. It also supports ultra-low delay interaction of IoT devices, with a delay of only about 10 ms or even 1 ms, achieving smart home connectivity with good performance.

(2) *The integration of 5G and family security*: With the rapid development of Internet of Everything technology, home security equipment has developed from the initial single-device unilateral sporadic monitoring to multi-device comprehensive systematic monitoring. A complete home security system composed of a variety of sensors and automatic monitoring equipment will greatly improve the accuracy and efficiency of its monitoring. However, in the 4G era, most home security systems remain in the passive monitoring stage and require human intervention. When the system detects an abnormal situation, the whole system cannot respond autonomously. At that time, someone needs to check and deal with it to restore the system to normal. The home security system in the 4G era is more like an automated system than an artificial intelligence butler. With the advent of the 5G era, Internet of Everything and AI technology will develop faster, home security will certainly enter the era of active monitoring, and the

dream of an artificial intelligence butler will be gradually realized. A future security system can monitor and deploy autonomously according to the user's habits to meet individual needs. When problems are encountered, they can be handled automatically. The whole process does not need human intervention, so security efficiency is greatly improved.

In the 5G era, for data processing, the home security system does not upload and store all the data in the cloud but instead adopts a combination of cloud computing and local computing. It not only saves time but also improves information security, which can effectively prevent personal information leakage and illegal invasion of the home security system. The direct connection between 5G and the cloud is realized by directly inserting a 5G card at the device end. It can avoid the influence of the Wi-Fi network environment on information transmission and make the data transmission speed of the home security system faster and more stable. The user experience will reach a higher level accordingly.

(3) *The integration of 5G and home network equipment*: The birth of 5G has undoubtedly brought new opportunities for home network equipment in solving the full geographical coverage, as the maximum downlink rate of 5G has already been comparable to that of optical fiber. According to the ITU's definition of 5G's key capability requirements, 5G user experience rate is up to 100 Mb/s–1 Gb/s, which is 10 to 100 times higher than 4G. In addition, the connection density of 5G reaches 1 million units/km^2, which is 10 times higher than that of 4G, and the cost of a single device is greatly reduced. The device that connects 5G to the home network is also called 5G Central Processing Element (CPE), which converts high-speed 5G signals into Ethernet and Wi-Fi signals.

5G CPE is used as a home network device to complete the home access to the Internet, mainly including indoor networking and outdoor relay networking. In the indoor networking mode (Fig. 3.9), 5G CPE is placed inside each home, and 5G CPE is directly connected to the 5G base station. This networking mode is suitable for the scene with a relatively dense family residence. In the outdoor relay networking mode (Fig. 3.10), 5G CPE responsible for the relay needs to be placed outdoors. In addition to completing the relay of home users near the 5G CPE, the 5G signal relay function also needs to be realized. This method is applicable to the long distance between home and 5G base station (usually over 5 km).

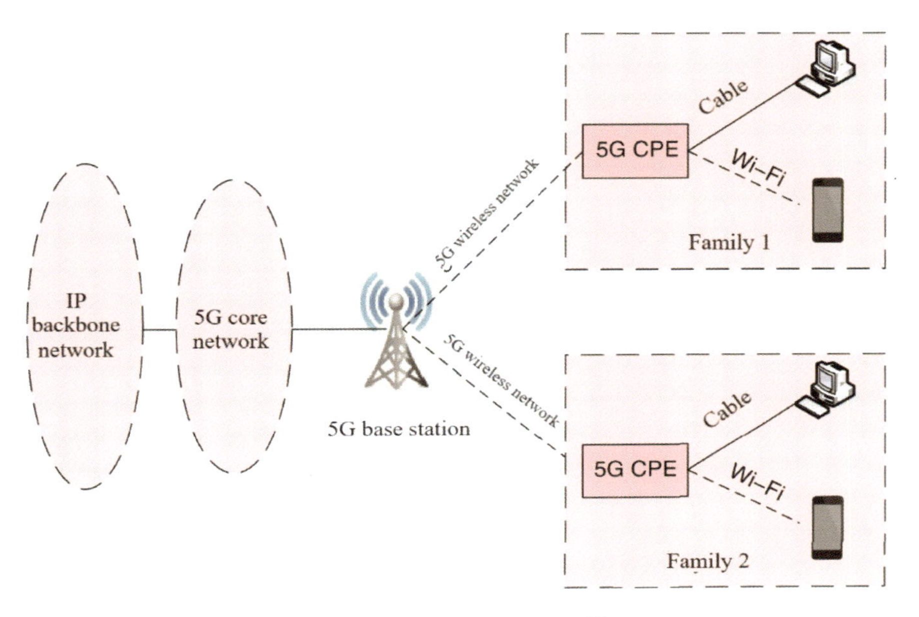

Figure 3.9 CPE indoor networking.

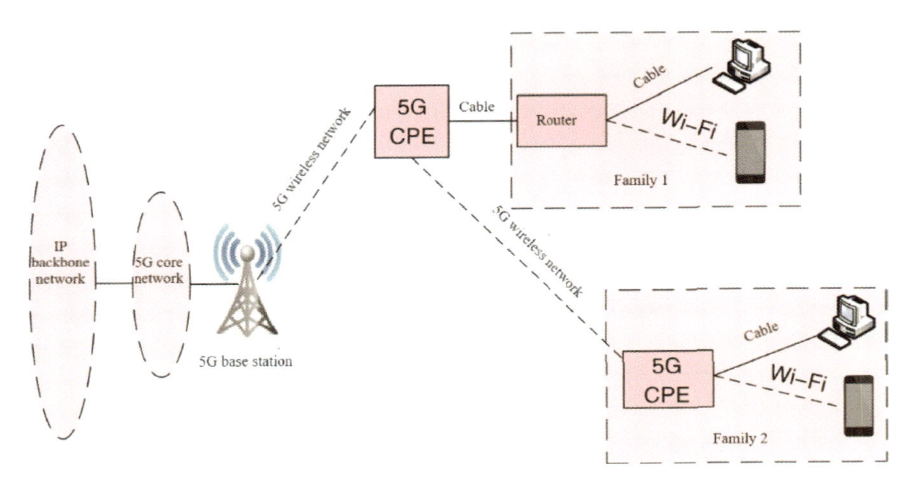

Figure 3.10 CPE outdoor relay networking.

3.2.4.3 *Summary and prospects*

Compared to the fragmentation of the traditional smart home, the smart home in the 5G era is characterized by systematization and full coverage.

Taking advantage of 5G's unique features of low delay, fast buffering, and low-power connection, 5G 8K smart TV will bring users a high-definition video picture and richer video details, and at the same time, it can realize a massive terminal connection. The communication between each part is more rapid and accurate, which greatly improves the intelligence and reliability of the security system. The advent of 5G CPE will redefine the networking mode, and people can gain a better network transmission experience at a low cost. The intelligence of home life in the 5G era will be closer to the automatic intelligent butler, which can provide services based on people's living habits and actual environment without any human intervention, thus leading to a better life.

3.2.5 *5G aids in the innovation of the media game industry*

3.2.5.1 *What will 5G bring to the game?*

With the popularization of the 5G network, 5G will help realize higher upload and download rates as well as shorter server response time for games, i.e., greatly reducing latency. Here, we can expect that the future game industry will become more refined due to 5G, and with lower latency, the game experience will be smoother. With higher upload and download rates, frames, screens, and special effects of the game will be greatly improved. Based on high-speed transmission rates, games need not be downloaded locally in the future but run on cloud servers, which saves the process of installing game files locally, greatly saving storage space of the computer and running time of the game.

3.2.5.2 *The changing trends of today's games*

Since mankind has entered the information age, Internet technology has been developing by leaps and bounds, and so is the derived game industry. Around 10 years ago, massive multiplayer online role-playing games (MMORPGs), led by the World of Warcraft, became popular all over the world and attracted millions of players, and 10 years later, multiplayer online battle arenas (MOBAs) and first-person shooting games (FPS) dominate the game market. What caused this change? It should have started from the game type.

MMORPG tends to spend time developing a character out of the players' own imagination, allowing the player to gain constant satisfaction and fun as their characters grow. However, such games have several problems that are almost impossible to solve. The first is being extremely unfriendly to new players because it takes a long time to grow from new players to old players. If you don't have friends in the game, it's hard to survive in the game. In the current game environment, only a few people are willing to spend a lot of time teaching someone who has very little knowledge about this. Many new players give up in the early exploration period. There's also a problem in the middle and later stages of the game, i.e., it's hard to attract new players, and old players tend to lose out.

How did MOBAs and FPS come up from behind? In the MMORPG era, the transmission speed, popularity of the network, and the hardware conditions of computers have limited the development of the game industry to some extent. After these technical problems are solved, the game industry also developed by leaps and bounds. Compared to that, what these two types of games have in common is that each game is a new start. There is no need to dwell on the past, and it is more friendly to new players because it is easy to get started. Besides, each game is not long, so people can use their spare time from work or study to relax themselves. Compared to MMORPG, MOBA and FPS are also more enjoyable and have higher requirements for players' on-the-spot operation ability. Compared to MMORPG that values teamwork, MOBA and FPS pay more attention to individual strength. The current live broadcast industry is well developed, so these two types of games became popular. This is evidence that games are becoming more like "fast food", i.e., it is less time-consuming, less demanding, and can be played anytime and anywhere.

3.2.5.3 *Changes in gaming devices*

In the past, computers were almost the only devices which were used to play games. Nowadays, all kinds of gaming devices are emerging and games are no longer limited to computers. Mobile phones are becoming one of the key gaming devices. The advent of 5G will surely bring about a qualitative leap in the mobile gaming industry similar to how the development of Internet technology once brought about changes to computer games. Most mobile games used to be similar to card collection and cultivation. The desired characters were acquired through a raffle by accumulating materials. Such materials could be quickly obtained through recharge, which was also the main means of making profits in this part of mobile games. Nowadays, mobile games are also becoming more real-time and complex. If we take Honor of Kings and Thrill of the Battlefield as examples, both of them are successful attempts by MOBA and FPS to enter mobile phones. Compared with PC, they further reduce operation requirements, become more simplified, and take less time, which is more suitable for today's fast-paced society. In subway stations, bus stations, and even on the roadside, it is common to see players holding mobile phones playing games.

3.2.5.4 *Summary and prospects*

Nowadays, the game industry is a vigorous and rapidly developing, emerging industry, which has driven the common development of many other industries, such as e-sports and live broadcasting. The advent of the 5G era is like adding a handful of dry firewood to the flame, which can make the games more refined and enhance their diversity and playability. The game market is approaching saturation, and 5G will be the key to tipping the balance. Game manufacturers need to follow the trend and keep up with the times. There is going to be a revolution in the game industry.

3.2.6 *5G supports the service efficiency of public utilities*

5G has a very positive significance in improving the service efficiency of public utilities, especially in the construction of smart cities. On one hand, 5G further improves the efficiency of network transmission on the basis of 4G. On the other hand, the large capacity of 5G enables more devices to be connected to the smart city network, thus expanding the functional boundary of the smart city and improving the efficiency of utility services.

5G has received a lot of attention not just because of its faster speed. In fact, for smartphones, the speed of 4G has been able to meet the demands of most consumption scenarios. Instead, 5G mainly realizes the purpose of connecting more IoT devices to the 5G network, so as to build a huge Internet of Things connecting everything. At the same time, low latency, large capacity, and high speed of the 5G technology will enable the rapid development of Internet of Everything, thus greatly improving the service efficiency of various utilities in smart cities.

3.2.6.1 *5G boosts smart grid*

With 5G's unique advantages, operators can truly achieve real-time monitoring and control of the grid. From the perspective of the national power grid, the power grid is actually composed of two networks: one is the traditional grid we have come into contact with and the other is the information communication network to ensure the reliable operation of the grid and provide data support for it. In the era of the smart grid, the role of information communication networks will be increasingly significant for the following reasons.

(1) First of all, the new energy generation features fragmentation, seasonal fluctuations, location fluctuations, etc., and the power grid is under increasing pressure, which requires millisecond response in regulation and control ability for the modern power grid, when it is connected to or transferred directly or withdrawn from the grid. In the future, there will be more user demands requiring a power grid of high speed and low latency, such as household electricity with time-of-use electricity price and instant charging of electric vehicles. It is precisely these characteristics of 5G that will enable the 5G-based power grid to bring about more stable and faster services to improve our life and productivity.
(2) In addition, the smart grid is one of the typical 5G applications in smart city deployment (Fig. 3.11). According to the *White Paper on 5G Powering Smart Grid Application*, 5G can update the previous operation mode and forge customized "industrial private network" services. Meanwhile, the application of 5G technology results in the smart grid being highly integrated with information and power flow, which is conducive not only to the efficient detection of energy consumption but also to the improvement of energy transport and use efficiency. This is in line with the needs of smart city construction and is of great significance for the interaction between the power grid and users. For example, by installing a smart grid, the city of Chattanooga, U.S., has significantly reduced the probability of power outages by about 50% during severe storms. As such, it is quite necessary to build smart power grids with the help of 5G technology in the deployment of smart cities to improve the quality of life of urban residents and promote sound urban development.

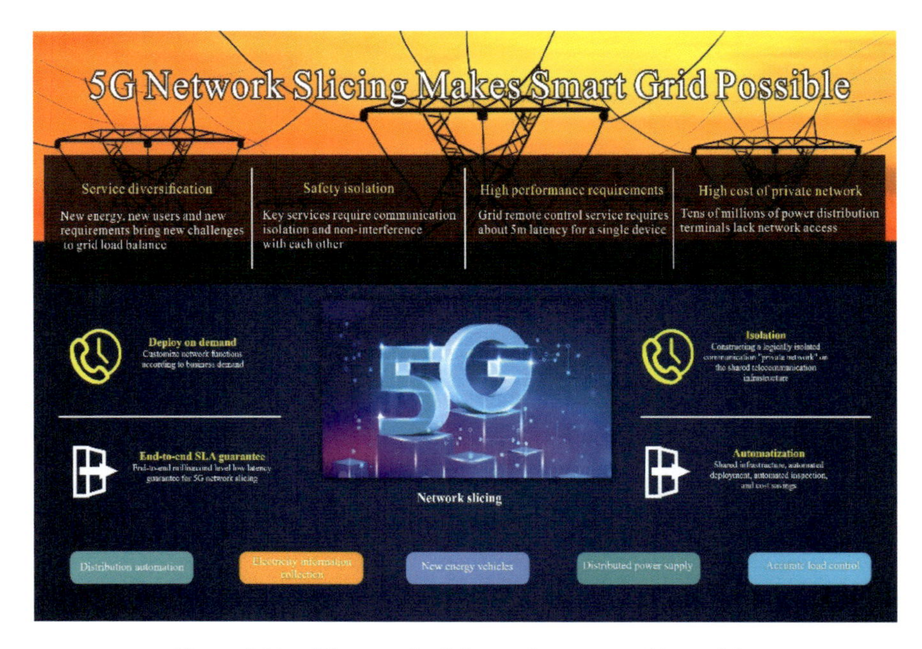

Figure 3.11 5G network slicing makes smart grid possible.

3.2.6.2 *5G makes elevator maintenance and rescue easy*

(1) 5G will also provide good technical support for intelligent maintenance and rescue of elevators. For example, 5G terminals can be used in elevator monitoring, control, and supervisory equipment to bring about huge changes in the control and monitoring of the whole elevator. A large number of 5G terminals can not only improve the reliability of online monitoring data transmission but also achieve low-power operation, which will make an inestimable contribution to the safety and energy-saving operation of the entire industry.

(2) The intelligent terminal can have real-time communication with parties responsible for elevator production, use, and maintenance to have a real-time guide for monitoring safety operation and emergency rescue work. In this way, the monitoring center can really achieve a central command, "zero" delay in information transmission. Real-time linkage among departments, unified command, unified rescue, unified investigation, and unified analysis can be realized to form an

emergency rescue mechanism with full coverage of the special equipment.

(3) Integrating 5G technology into elevator inspection and detection will make it possible to assist remote online inspection of elevators. If inspectors have doubts or uncertainties about special events on the scene, they can use terminals to ask for help from big databases or experts behind them. The data transmission speed will reach over 1 Gb/s for smooth video and voice communication. Therefore, elevator maintenance staff facing technical problems can ask for help online and solve them at once without the need to go back multiple times, which can greatly improve the maintenance efficiency.

(4) The intelligent terminal and early fault warning and analysis system based on 5G will improve the safety and reliability of elevator operation. With 5G, the emergency alarm phone device required by inspection rules will be directly upgraded to real-time video communication. In case of emergency, this will be convenient to provide real-time rescue guidance and psychological counseling to passengers, so as to enhance their sense of security. In addition, as micro stations are dominant in 5G which has high coverage density and can fully cover mobile phones in the elevator car, people can continue their communication unobstructed in the car and have a better experience and sense of security.

3.2.6.3 *5G promotes fire rescue*

Fire rescue teams are the main force for governments at all levels to prevent and respond to all kinds of disasters and accidents. In the face of complex, changing, and extremely emergent tasks, it is highly important to build a modern fire emergency communication support, command, and dispatch system relying on efficient and reliable mobile communication technology. The implementation and promotion of 5G communication technology will play a great role in promoting the development of fire information communication for the following reasons:

(1) 5G signals feature high-speed transmission and can digitize the protective equipment of individual soldiers. Smart wearable equipment can acquire vital signs information, environment information, movement speed, location of staff in field operation and transmit it through high-speed network traffic to the site command, which helps

commanders understand the position and status of each operational personnel in the scene area, then reasonably allocate personnel, provide timely instructions, and avoid the loss of life to the greatest extent.

(2) 5G features large capacity and can allow the system to access multiple terminals. All kinds of sensors and infrared photography can be used to collect field data, conduct digital processing and analysis, and monitor real-time environment parameters, including toxic gas, fire spread trend, building structure, and evacuee perception, and can greatly improve the ability to transmit command information, judge the disaster level, and analyze the situation.

(3) The low latency of 5G can make instructions more efficient. The spectrum bandwidth based on millimeter-wave 5G communication is 10 times that of 4G, and the latency can be accurate to the millisecond level, which can meet the transmission rate and bandwidth required for two-way remote command instructions.

(4) The high connection reliability of 5G can realize the high-speed and reliable connection between personnel and equipment, so as to control remote equipment such as robots, unmanned vehicles, drones, and unmanned ships and fully protect the safety of the commanders and fighters.

3.2.6.4 *Summary and prospects*

5G will be a technological weapon for building smart cities and improving the efficiency of public utility services. Integrating 5G technology into the construction of smart cities can achieve smart transportation, smart elevator maintenance and promote fire rescue. We can see that the advent of the 5G era will better promote the development of urban facilities, improve the stability and convenience of public utilities, and drive the sound development of smart cities.

3.2.7 *5G facilitates the service quality improvement of the financial industry*

The business model of the financial industry is closely related to the upgrade of the communication network. Looking back at the financial industry development, offline physical outlets provided financial services in the 2G era, soliciting business online became popular in the 3G era, and applications (apps) were used to approach users and provide comprehensive services in the 4G era. The arrival of the 5G era will further inject vitality into the financial industry and once again upgrade the financial business model with the arrival of technologies like artificial intelligence.

3.2.7.1 *Digital banking: The 5G era is within reach*

With the arrival of 5G applications, the financial service experience provided by the financial industry for the customers will be greatly improved in the future. Especially with the support of features like ultra-high speed and extremely low latency in 5G communication, the efficiency of customer payment and transaction will be significantly improved.

The first is the construction of smart outlets. Smart outlets will disrupt the concept of the traditional banking division and establish a set of boundless services and unlimited experience for customers through the comprehensive application of emerging technologies, such as artificial intelligence, biometrics, Internet of Things, holographic projection, AR/VR, and Big Data.

The second is payment modes. In the 5G era, AR/VR will no longer be limited by speed and latency, and data transmission, storage, and computing functions can be transferred from local to cloud, so as to provide richer data assistance for decision-making and realize a more real-time experience in the scenario. At the same time, payment modes combined with biometrics, such as the current face-scanning payment (Fig. 3.12), will be more convenient and diversified. In the future, there will be many new payment forms, such as micro-expression payment, brainwave payment, iris payment, and voiceprint payment. Customers will be able to make purchases without cash or mobile phones, providing new payment experiences.

The last is the intelligent risk control system. "5G+ Internet of Things" will be used to extend the bank information from a single enterprise to the entire industrial chain and realize data information integration of upstream, downstream, and cooperative enterprises of the industrial chain, so as to build mutual trust and a win — win situation between banks and enterprises and reduce the credit risks caused by information asymmetry.

Figure 3.12 Face-scanning payment.

3.2.7.2 *Butler-style financial services*

The 5G era will provide residents with a more convenient one-stop, "butler-style" payment and consumption experience.

In terms of banking business, traditional businesses such as payment and credit-granting will be deeply integrated and cross-connected with various industries to fully expand new channels and forms, including 5G smartphones, wearable devices, and virtual reality equipment, so that it will become a functional link in the banking supply chain.

In daily life, bank accounts can realize remote inquiry and automatic payment by connecting with the household's water, electricity, gas, and heat meter. Medical institutions, banks, and users are all inter-connected, so that doctors can learn users' physical status through wearable devices, and banks can provide users with payment, insurance, loan, and other services based on medical and user data.

3.2.7.3 *A secure financial system*

As shown in Fig. 3.13, in the 5G era, the stability of financial system development will also be greatly improved. With more bank users, the data volume of the financial industry will show explosive growth and in this way can help relevant technicians to use these data to analyze in detail the natural attributes and financial behaviors of enterprises and individuals, so as to improve the accuracy and integrity of data analysis in the financial industry. At the same time, the financial industry can apply 5G technology to collect financial data in exponential growth, and the financial credit rating system with higher credibility and more appraisal dimensions will also be created, which can effectively shield or filter false information and completely solve the problems of strong subjectivity and poor reliability in the current rating system.

Figure 3.13 5G contributes to the robustness of financial system development.

Compared to 4G, 5G has faster network transmission speed and lower latency. Therefore, defects including network congestion, interaction delay, and poor security existing in 4G technology will be effectively solved in the 5G era. 5G network can greatly reduce latency, and at the same time, user payment will be highly efficient. With ultra-low latency, the security audit mode based on users' biological information can effectively curb fraud and guarantee fund security.

3.2.7.4 *Summary and prospects*

With the rapid development of technology, digital banking and intelligent banking have become the only way for the development of traditional banks. 5G technology will bring revolutionary changes to the financial service industry to improve the user experience of efficient payment and effectively enhance the security of mobile payment. In the future, the competition among banks will no longer be limited to business form, customer base, and products. Against the backdrop of increasingly serious homogenization, only with the application and promotion of 5G technology can financial service industry achieve stability and long-term development by solving the outstanding problems such as technical failures and risk loopholes existing in the intelligent transformation of traditional banks.

Chapter 4

Beyond Imagination: The Way Ahead in the Era of "Technology as the King"

In the previous chapters, we have described the technical features of 5G through the enormous changes it has produced in vertical industries as well as social life. In the future, more convenient lives for people, a more intelligent society and revitalized traditional industries will all be attributed to the utilization of 5G. For example, upgrading various industries using 5G will improve productivity while providing more employment opportunities and creating more material wealth as well. The present times are developing at an accelerated rate with technology progressing apace, resulting in the tendency of society to move ahead with giant strides. Facing the powerful current of the times, we cannot help but ask: after 5G, where will technology head for? Impacted by 5G, artificial intelligence, biotechnology and other high-tech torrents, will the fate of all human beings be delivered to technology and let it act as the king, with all human beings running amok, such as a wild direction-challenged horse? Or will we still retain human rationality and thinking, and hold on to the reins of power while letting technology benefit us? As a metaphor, let's assume it is hard to imagine that an accelerating train can run forever without derailment. Since Watt invented the steam engine, the accelerated development of science and technology has been lasting for nearly 300 years. While enjoying all kinds of convenience and benefits brought about by technology, we are obliged to seriously consider: where is the "safety limit" of the accelerated development of science and technology?

Does data generation, the surge of storage, computation and transmission, require us to set a "data ceiling" proactively?

4.1 Where is Technology Going Ahead in the Post-5G Era?

Today, as the core of the technology research and development, 5G technology is a hot spot in our society and also the competition focus among various forces in the information field. Even so, we should still have the courage to have a vision of the 6G era, a new era of the Internet of Everything and Wisdom in the future.

4.1.1 *Explosion of the application requirements*

To visualize the new era freely, we should start by discussing the vision of the 6G era. It is common knowledge that 5G realizes the Internet of Everything, while 6G makes the world's information ubiquitous, allowing a comprehensive coverage. In the 6G world, virtuality and reality are mutually complementary, with people and people, people and things, as well as things and things, all fully digitized to form a huge digital world. In order to realize more intelligent and efficient information delivery, the combination of artificial intelligence and communication technology will greatly help human beings to further boost productivity, improving the overall resource allocation of the society and realizing intelligent autonomy.

The vision of 6G is to empower a wide range of industries and application scenarios. It is predicted that in a 6G system, the number of data flow and wireless devices will rocket. As a consequence, there may be hundreds of devices per cubic meter. Therefore, the peak link throughput of each 6G system will exceed terabits per second (Tb/s). Take road traffic as an example, ubiquitous intelligent vehicles and robots are computing nodes with high mobility. In order to achieve accurate recognition and scheduling, accurate beam control and 3D scene interaction are urgently needed. It is estimated that the peak transmission rate of mobile communication in this scenario will be 100 Gb/s–1 Tb/s, and the delay of transmission will be less than 10 μs. Therefore, an ultra-wideband mobile network and ultra-low delay of technology are urgently needed.

In wireless automation plants, ultra-low time delay of communication is of paramount importance, as each device needs to achieve high-precision synchronization up to 1 μs. Take display technology as an example, with the large-scale application of sensors and imaging equipment, the seamless connection between devices and human senses becomes possible. AR/VR technology will come into the houses of ordinary people, and wearable displays will realize visual imaging with unprecedented resolution, high frame number, and wide dynamic range. At the same time, high-speed imaging, health monitoring, image recognition and intelligent processing, positioning, and sensing will accurately capture every detail of human life, which obviously exceeds the communication capacity of the existing wireless network. Hence, greater data volume and higher data transmission density will be the key technology for the next generation of mobile communication.

Figure 4.1 compares the core requirements of 5G and 6G. It can be seen that the 6G system has higher requirements for data density, rate and delay, which allows the 6G system to meet any demand of air, sky, earth, and sea, but higher requirements for higher speed and more reliable communication are also present. To meet the above core requirements, the main development trend of 6G will have the following characteristics:

(1) *Full spectrum*: The operating frequency range covers the high-optical frequency and full-spectrum systems from microwave, millimeter wave, terahertz to laser.

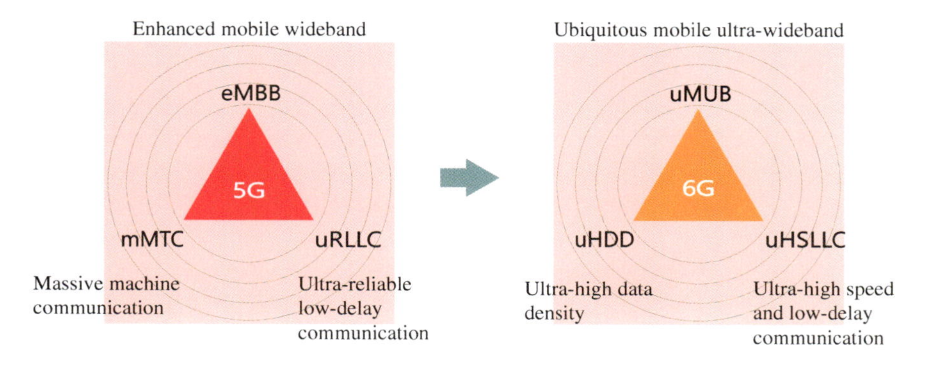

Figure 4.1 Comparison of core technical requirements of 5G and 6G.

(2) *Full coverage*: Ubiquitous mobile UWB on the ground, sea, air, and space.
(3) *Full fusion*: Communication, control, sensing, computing, imaging and other technologies will be integrated to form a multi-purpose and multi-functional system.
(4) *Full intelligence*: An intelligent network system will be formed from the application layer to the physical layer, from top to bottom.

4.1.2 *Great leaps in system performance*

In combination with multiple application scenarios, ubiquitous mobile ultra-broadband (uMUB), ultra-high speed, low latency communication (uHSLLC), and ultra-high data density (uHDD) are the three key technical indicators of wireless communication system in the 6G era. Based on the above three key technical indicators, end-to-end communication, sensing, computing collaboration, and photon artificial intelligence are integrated, and two candidate 6G schemes can be primarily constructed: (1) multifunctional fusion, full-spectrum, and all-photon wireless access network and (2) a 100 Gb/s, hyper-spectral, air–space–sea integrated network of laser–millimeter wave fusion.

In order to realize the ultra-high peak speed rate, it is necessary not only to improve the spectral efficiency but also to expand the system bandwidth. To achieve greater radio bandwidth, further use of the apZ and terahertz frequencies is required. While 6G will also take advantage of lower frequencies to achieve large areas of mobile cellular coverage, ultra-efficient short-range connectivity solutions will be key to 6G, where higher frequencies can play a role. Space loss has a significant impact on signal transmission, especially over long transmission distances (at 400 GHz, the space loss is about 100 dB/10 m). As shown in Fig. 4.2, the increase of free space loss from 30 GHz to the terahertz region is small, but the free space loss at different frequencies is different. Relatively speaking, there are several favorable spectrum windows between atmospheric absorption peaks of terahertz radio spectrum, all of which can be used for signal transmission. On November 26, 2019, ITU fully discussed about this in the 2019 World Radio Communication Conference (WRC-19) and finally agreed to use a total of 137 GHz spectrum resources in 275–296 GHz, 306–313 GHz, 318–333 GHz, and 356–450 GHz for fixed and land mobile services. In a sense, this will greatly foster the rapid

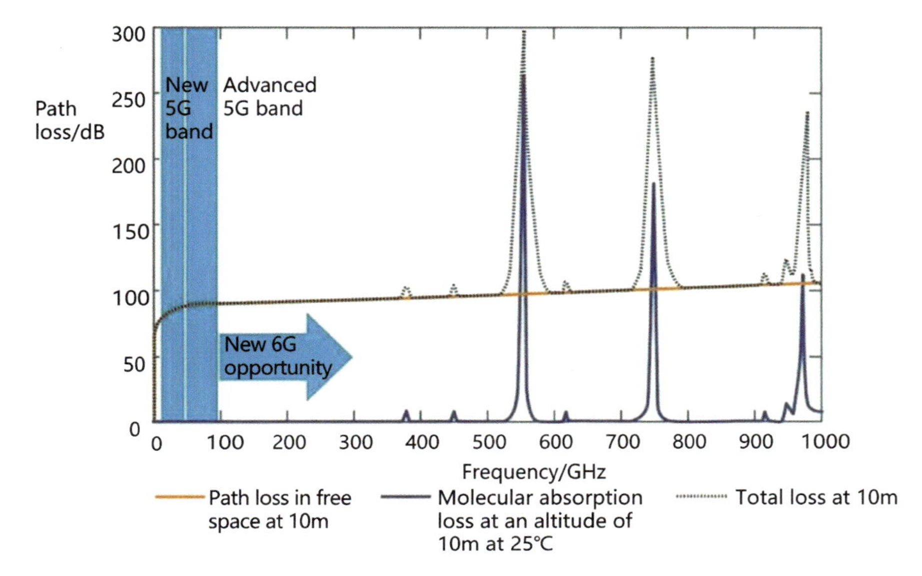

Figure 4.2 Free space losses of each frequency band of radio spectrum.

development of terahertz technology, so it will play an important role in the future of 6G mobile communication.

Multigrade integration is also one of the development trends of 6G technology. Starting from 4G communication technology, cellular, Wi-Fi, and Bluetooth have become the standard configuration of mobile phones. In the 6G system, the research focus will be on a more intensive realization of multiple frequencies and multiple application modes. Satellite communication is a potential integrated system. In order to cover all regions of the world, integrated satellite communication needs to improve its coverage capability. In previous generations of mobile communication systems, satellite communication functions are not integrated into mobile phones due to complex issues, such as terminal size and cost. In recent years, with the deployment of more and more LEO satellites and the reduction of satellite link budget, there will be a possibility to integrate satellites with cellular systems.

In addition, the development trends of 6G potential technology include ultra-large antenna, terahertz technology, new coding modulation mechanism, all-frequency communication, space–sky integration, flexible network, artificial intelligence, and so on. These technologies assist each other to jointly build the preliminary architecture of 6G network to meet the following initial ideas:

(1) *Adaptive service network*: The 6G system can realize the optimal configuration of the network service according to the users' requirements.
(2) *Quick response to plug-in and play*: On the basis of the existing cellular network architecture, we further realize innovation and simplification so as to realize the minimal mobile communication network architecture and accelerate the speed of information delivery.
(3) *Autonomous flexible network*: In the 6G system, end-to-end network defined by the whole software, forward compatibility of network protocols, de-cell network architecture, user-centered network autonomy, and self-evolution will be gradually realized.
(4) *Smart Internet*: It will enable AI to be everywhere, achieving a smart Internet with network computing power and ubiquitous intelligence.
(5) *Super-high network security*: The increase in data volume will make life convenient, but it also brings great challenges to information security. To make the network more immune to risks, it is necessary to study the risk prediction algorithm.

However, it is worth noting that the development of 6G technology still faces many challenges. First, due to higher-frequency band, the path loss will further increase, during which the RF amplifier and antenna will be required to provide additional gain. The research and development of the third-generation compound semiconductor or even the next-generation compound semiconductor technology, as well as the larger scale antenna array, will also be a difficult step in the development of 6G RF hardware. Second, energy consumption is also a big challenge. For a low-rate sensor system, it needs to be able to collect energy. As for the communication base station, higher efficiency will greatly reduce the operating cost of the equipment. Finally, in the terahertz band, the material properties and device parasitic effects of the existing semiconductor processes will change greatly. We need to find out how to put forward more suitable silicon or III–V semiconductor technology and combine electronics and optics to make it complementary, which will work as a development direction of 6G technology.

4.1.3 *Intelligent wireless networks*

In the 6G world, the digital and physical worlds are intertwined, and people's lives depend on reliable operation of the Internet. However, whether in the digital world or the physical world, the network is likely to be attacked, and an information security problem will disturb the operation of the entire 6G network. To solve this problem, we need to add a trust model to the wireless network so that users can trust the communication on the network. At this time, the trust model needs to continuously collect information between individuals and organizational entities to quickly and accurately trace the source of attacks so as to ensure network security.

In the 6G communication network, machine learning and artificial intelligence are the key technologies. Among them, machine learning relies on digging into a large amount of data and realizing information recognition based on the collected data. To process the data, 6G networks must also have "intelligent" capabilities, such as self-configuring or managing complex networks. In addition, another technology in the center of public attention is blockchain, which is conducive to further integration of technologies to achieve wireless networks with intelligence and mutual trust.

Artificial intelligence technology has empowered wireless communication technology with great potential. The application of machine learning in RF signal processing, spectrum mining, and RF spectrum mapping can greatly enhance the prediction of communication capacity and realize automatic optimization, network resource scheduling, and slicing. By optimizing and managing the communication system, the system complexity can be greatly reduced, then the cost of network deployment can be reduced, and the optimized management of communication network by carriers can be transformed into the optimized management of service requirements so as to reduce the complexity of network optimization and realize intelligent optimization on a high-level. From 1G to 4G, the mobile communication network connects people. This service is relatively simple, so it is easy to manage. Only the software system can be used to manage business and users. However, starting from 5G, the management objects of the mobile communication network also include massive intelligent devices, which are connected with the collected big data through scenes and services. These even need to be presented in the form of holographic technology and full sense technology, which require artificial intelligence technology.

In the first stage, AI technology has been preliminarily applied to smartphones. Considering that AI has the computing power of trillions per second, AI photography, image optimization, and harassment information interception can be easily realized. In the future, AI-based real-time translation and on-demand multimedia will assist in the operation of a mobile phone. Second, artificial intelligence can also realize remote control and intervention, such as real-time remote monitoring, intervention, medical services, and remote sensing of intelligent devices. Finally, in 5G or 6G networks, AI technology could also be used for autonomous vehicle driving. In the second stage, artificial intelligence will be introduced and used in wireless communication networks. In the evolution of 6G network, if we want to optimize the network by relying on isolated indicators, we cannot achieve satisfactory results. At this point, in order to achieve faster, refined, and efficient network performance, it is necessary to use artificial intelligence technology at all levels of the network. As for how to further apply artificial intelligence technology to the network, it needs to be further discussed and solved. In the last stage, artificial intelligence technology will be popularized in all application scenarios and intelligent interaction will be realized. At this stage, more and more businesses will no longer require human involvement because it can be done independently by machines and intelligent agents. Also, many business scenarios might require multiple agents to work together. In order to achieve this vision, 6G needs to overcome a series of performance challenges and accurately adapt network bandwidth, latency, reliability, coverage, energy consumption, security, and other indicators according to the various business scenarios. Eventually, we will see the connectivity of "people, things and intelligence". Whether in the physical world or the digital world, human society and artificial intelligence will be fully interconnected.

The incipient research and development of 6G still needs a long way to go for realizing the vision of 6G. The research and development of each generation of mobile communication requires the cooperation of numerous enterprises and scientific research institutions all over the world. With the joint efforts of many basic disciplines such as theoretical science, material science and information engineering, it is possible to constantly break through physical limit and technical limit that once seemed insurmountable. This is an extremely difficult and lengthy process. It will take at least 10–20 years to move forward step by step from theoretical research, technology maturity, and industrialization to large-scale commercial use.

Looking into the future, in the evolution of mobile communication technology from 5G to 6G and even higher, human exploration will never stop. The future world will also become more wonderful due to the development of wireless communication technology.

4.2 What is the Way Ahead for Human Beings in the Post-5G Era?

As mentioned previously, 5G technology is not just an evolution based on the first four generations of mobile communication technology, but also a leapfrog development as well. 5G is a carrier or a catalyst to empower society and all walks of life, more than a communication technology, which is changing both people's lives and the whole society. While 5G is ascending, 6G has already been put on the agenda. Moreover, human beings will also create and experience faster wireless transmission technologies. At the same time, artificial intelligence technology and biotechnology, especially burgeoning gene editing technology indicates that human beings' ability to transform nature and themselves is improving constantly. It is just like a dancer wearing magic shoes, rotating at a high-speed. But as we gallop and advance with technology, we also need to see the other side. In the post-Moore era, technological progress has been progressing rapidly like a river running fast, but it is bound to fall apart. While technology brings us speed and convenience, how will human beings move forward in the era where technology acts as the king? Let the wings of imagination flap and take us forward to have a look.

4.2.1 *Dramatic changes in human life beyond imagination*

Great changes have taken place in people's lives along with the continuous development of science and technology. The ways of eating, wearing, living, and traveling have changed at an unprecedented speed. The assistance of electronic products has helped people save a lot of time in their daily life. In the near future, the onset of intelligent home robots will make it no longer an empty promise to "hold out one's hands for clothes and open one's mouth to be fed". At the same time, smart home appliances offer a comfortable living environment for human beings, including temperature and humidity control and even adaptive control of negative oxygen ions, to build a spring-like and pleasant environment. Human beings can enjoy the comfort like greenhouse flowers, no longer feeling like our predecessors shivering in the cold or sweating heavily in hot weather. There is no doubt that faster transportation nowadays has allowed Li Bai's visions in his poems to come true: returning from Jiangling that is a thousand miles far just within a day. Airplanes, high-speed trains and cars have become convenient means of transportation now, and it is normal for many people to shuttle back and forth between any two places on the earth. With the dawn of the 5G era, self-driving cars will gradually become part of people's daily lives. As long as the destination is input into the self-driving system, it will automatically plan the route and safely send the passengers to their destinations by car. With the rapid development of mobile communication and Internet technology, the biggest convenience for human beings is that people can know the world events without leaving their homes. Mobile phones, computers, iPads and other terminal devices make it convenient for people to access the Internet anytime and anywhere. They can learn about events and celebrities' anecdotes from all over the world, read online, watch TV dramas, do online shopping, and use VR experience to travel without visiting in person. Even if you stay at home, you can get all the information you need without any real contact with the outside world.

Apart from the above convenience of food, clothing, housing, and transportation, burgeoning science and technology has also presented human beings with a longer life span. With the improvement of living conditions and medical treatment, the average life expectancy of human beings has now exceeded 70 years. With further development of science and technology, an average life span of over 100 years will not be a dream. More exciting progresses will happen through artificial intelligence and technologies such as gene editing. With the development of artificial intelligence, living individuals are experiencing continuous evolution from the first, the second, to the third generations. In the broad sense, life can be seen as a self-replicating information processing system, with its physical structure as hardware and behavior and thought as software. In the book, *Life 3.0*, Max Tegmark, a physicist at the Massachusetts Institute of Technology, divides life into three stages. At present, human beings are only in the second stage, called "Life 2.0". We can learn new knowledge and upgrade our minds ("software"), but we cannot upgrade our bodies ("hardware"). So, human development is greatly limited. With the rapid development of artificial intelligence, information technology and biotechnology are highly integrated. The possibility of "Life 3.0" to upgrade the "software" and "hardware" has already seen initial results. Human beings can design both "software" and "hardware", and a body can be changed from carbon into silicon (or a mixture of carbon and silicon), finally getting rid of the shackles of evolution.

The development of science and technology yields obvious dividends for human beings, particularly the undoubted convenience and comfort of life. But does it also imply a profound human crisis? The convenience of network technology also brings potential danger. The vast volume of fragmented information which is hard to distinguish between true and false can overwhelm people, making us addicted to and lost in it. Time is wasted, attention is distracted, and it's hard to maintain concentration. At the same time, the convenience of online search has replaced deep thinking and systematic learning of many people, leaving brain hollowing no longer a sensational pseudo-proposition.

All these are serious challenges to human beings. Otaku, who never have contacted the outside world, lack real contact with the outside world, face-to-face communication with others and empathy. Although the gene editing technology of upgrading human life is of great significance and value to human evolution, there may be ethical problems and even evil hidden behind, which can bring about a crisis. While we stay optimistic about the future direction of human beings, we still need to be thoughtful and cautious.

4.2.2 *Will it come true? — Replacing human beings by machines*

So, as we are aware, the history of human development also reflects the history of technological changes.

However, people don't always show a welcoming attitude to technological changes but mixed feelings of love and hate. It is thought conventionally that fear of technology dates back to the upending of the economic order at the start of the British Industrial Revolution in the 18th century, when it was already entrenched. The original intention of inventing textile machinery was to improve weaving efficiency, but textile workers launched a boycott movement because they were afraid of losing their jobs. People hated the scientific and technological advancements which can improve productivity, and there even appeared "Luddites" who specially destroyed power textile machines. Later generations extended the meaning of "Luddites" to include the people who hate technological innovation or hold anti-technological innovation views.

Continued economic growth later proved that the Luddites' hatred of technology was wrong and baseless. Actually, technology had greatly improved people's living standards. Over centuries, we have seen the economic prosperity and unprecedented wealth created by technological changes. It was a generally accepted orthodox idea that in all economic fields, science and technology benefited workers. However, at the end of 20th century, people began to lose confidence.

We know that the two elements of productivity are capital and workers, which are complementary rather than substitutive. New capital (machines are an important one) tends to make workers more efficient. It replaces some workers, and it also creates newer and more creative jobs to consume the new capital, so workers' wages go up anyway. But that is no longer the case. Instead, a new possibility has emerged, capital can replace workers entirely. That is to say, with a specially designed set of machines, capital can do the jobs that workers do even better than them. In this sense, the replacement of workers by machines is not a myth.

We drew a skill map of workers' skills in the order from high to low and took a look at how scientific and technological progress impacts them from low to high. For more than 200 years, science and technology have been changing the nature of workers and the value of their specific skills. The first turning point touched the craftsmen. At first, the rise of the industrial revolution devalued the craftsmen who made products entirely by hand, while other workers who did not have many skills made profits by quickly learning to operate new machines. The second turning point reached unskilled workers. At the beginning of 20th century, the widespread use of electricity led to the emergence of more sophisticated machinery, which required well-educated and skilled workers to operate. At this time, unskilled workers were in a disadvantaged position, while educated workers were in high demand. The third turning point affected workers with intermediate skills. Since the 1980s, information technology had evolved to the point where machines could take over moderately skilled jobs, such as bookkeeping, accounting, and repetitive factory work. The number of jobs in these categories was shrinking, the number of people working at them was also shrinking, and wages were stagnating. But this trend is limited, and at both ends of the skill spectrum, people with high and low skills were doing much better. The information technology was not advanced enough to take over the work of highly skilled people such as legal advisers, doctors, and financial experts, and could not perform tasks such as problem judgment, coordination, and problem solving. At the lower end of the skill map, information technology was also less of a threat because computers were least skilled in jobs requiring high physical agility, such as home healthcare, horticulture, and cooking.

Now comes the fourth turning point. With the rapid development of information technology, the impact has reached both ends of the skill map, and no one can rest with ease. The integrated development of Big Data, cloud computing, artificial intelligence, 5G, and other high-tech technologies is taking over at an alarming rate the jobs on the top end of the skill map, such as doctors, lawyers, managers, engineers, and professors. We thought that these jobs require a high-level of knowledge and these highly skilled people will not be threatened by computer competition, but we are clearly wrong. Using hardware and software such as Big Data and supercomputing, they are faster and more accurate than human beings. An even more surprising replacement occurred at the other end of the skill spectrum, that is, in low-skilled and low-paid jobs which require little cognitive effort but are labor-consuming. In the last few decades, computers were not able to do this. But a worrying turn of events occurred. The development of science and technology has continuously improved the performance of robots, including the emergence of various intelligent systems. Therefore, driving, cleaning, and manual operation in dangerous environments at the lower end of the skill map can be completely replaced by machines, and they can even do a better job.

Parallel to this, it is important to note that technological changes are accelerating instead of slowing down. As a result, the impacts on human jobs are increasing not decreasing. A media journalist once asked Nicholas Negroponte, founder of the Massachusetts Institute of Technology Media Lab, "After 5 or 10 years, in what ways can human beings surpass computers?" He answered, "Almost nothing but enjoyment". This answer may depress us. Human beings cannot imagine and cannot bear a life only with enjoyment and no creation, which will be meaningless.

Although the threat or replacement mentioned above will not fully occur throughout our lifetime, it is already happening and will be overwhelming. Where should we go? Racing against technologies to surpass the capability of machines? The answer is "impossible". To find out the answer, we need to look not at machines, but at ourselves.

We need to go back to the beginning, to look inside ourselves, and maybe gain strength and find hope. Humanity is of amazing value, and it is due to this nature that human beings have surpassed all forms of life on earth and created a glorious history. Then, only with a deep understanding of this nature and full respect for it can human beings take our destiny by the throat. With the help of high technology, we will race across the winds and waves to a brighter and better future.

Bibliography

Afif Osseiran, Jose F. Monserrac, and Patrick Marsch (2017). *5G Mobile and Wireless Communications Technology*. Chen Ming, Miao Qingyu, and Liu Wu (Trans.) Beijing: The People's Posts and Telecommunications Press.

Ai Bin (2012). *Evolution of WCDMA System and Study of Call Admission Control Algorithm*. Xi'an: Xidian University.

Chen Liang and Yu Shao-hua (2019). Preliminary study on the trend of 6G mobile communication. *Optical Fiber Telecommunications* 2019(4): 1–8.

Chen Xu, Wei Zhiqing, Feng Zhiyong *et al.* (2020). Intelligent machine-type communication and network for 6G system. *Chinese Journal on Internet of Things* 4(1): 59–71.

Dai Yueyue, Zhang Ke, and Zhang Yan (2020). Blockchain empowered 6G. *Chinese Journal on Internet of Things* 4(1): 111–120.

Ding Qi (2011). *Mobile Communication*. Beijing: The People's Posts and Telecommunications Press.

Duan Baoyan (2020). Evolution and innovation of antenna systems for beyond 5G and 6G. *Frontiers of Information Technology and Electronic Engineering* 21(1): 1–6.

Hu Fei (2020). *5G Network Opportunities: Research and Development Prospects*. Beijing: The People's Posts and Telecommunications Press.

Marcos Katz and Frank H. P. Fitzek (2009). *WiMAX Evolution: Emerging Technologies and Applications*. West Sussex, United Kingdom: John Wiley & Sons, Ltd.

Matti Latva-Aho and Kari Leppänen (2019). *Key Drivers and Research Challenges for 6G Ubiquitous Wireless Intelligence*. Oulu: University of Oulu.

Li Yubin (1997). The development of China's mobile communication industry in 1996. *Posts and E-Commerce Information* 1997(12): 23–24.

Liu Dong, Wu Qihui, and Tony Q. S. Quek (2020). Spectrum cognitive intelligent management and control for aviation 6G. *Chinese Journal on Internet of Things* 4(1): 12–18.

Liu Guangyi, Huang Yuhong, Xiang Jiying *et al.* (2019). *5G Mobile Communication System: From Evolution to Revolution*. Beijing: The People's Posts and Telecommunications Press.

Science and Technology Daily (2020). 5G has come 6G starts exploring. *Technology and Market*, 27(3): 2–3.

Seung June Yi, Sung Duck Chun, Young Dae Lee *et al.* (2013). *Radio Protocols for LTE and LTE-Advanced.* Singapore: John Wiley & Sons Singapore Pte. Ltd.

Tang Zhixuan (2004). A survey of the third generation mobile communication technology (3G). *Mobile Communications* 1(1): 13–16.

Tan Yanmei and Cao Hua (2008). Mobile communication technology from 1G to 3G. *Guangxi Zhiliang Jiandu Daobao* 2008(8): 80.

The Center for Information and Industry Development (CCID), Series (2020). Key drivers and research challenges for 6G ubiquitous wireless intelligence. *China Computer Journal*, March 16, 2020 (008).

University of Oulu, Finland and 70 Communication Experts (2020). Key Drivers and Research Challenges for 6G Ubiquitous Wireless Intelligence. Communications Weekly, March 30, 2020 (018).

Wei Kejun (2020). Review of global 6G research progresses. *Mobile Communications* 44(3): 34–36+42.

Wei Kejun and Hu Bo (2020). 6G Vision requirements and technology trend prospect. *Telecommunications Science* 36(02): 126–129.

Wu Qihui (2020). "The Internet of things and 6G" topic guide. *Chinese Journal on Internet of Things* 4(1): 1–2.

Wu Weiling and Niu Kai (2005). *Principle of Mobile Communication*. Beijing: Publishing House of Electronics Industry.

You Xiaohu, Yin Hao, and Wu Hequan (2020). On 6G and wide-area IoT. *Chinese Journal on Internet of Things* 4(01): 3–11.

Zhai You and Xie Hu (2019). *5G Society: From "Litters Live" to "Internet of Everything"*. Beijing: Publishing House of Electronics Industry.

Zhang Ping, Niu Kai, Tian Hui *et al.* (2019). Technology prospect of 6G mobile communications. *Journal of Communications* 40(1): 141–148.

Index